THE BIBLE STORY

VOLUME VII

Wonderful Jesus

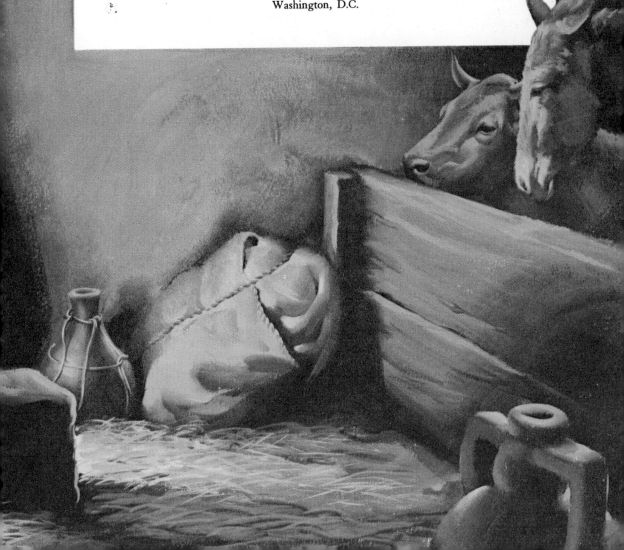

The

BIBLE STORY

More Than Four Hundred Stories in Ten Volumes
Covering the Entire Bible From Genesis to Revelation

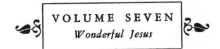

VOLUME SEVEN
Wonderful Jesus

BY ARTHUR S. MAXWELL

Author of *Uncle Arthur's Bedtime Stories, The Children's Hour With Uncle Arthur,
The Secret of the Cave,* etc.

•

REVIEW AND HERALD PUBLISHING ASSOCIATION
Washington, D.C.

CONTENTS

5

The impress of perfection was upon the character of Jesus even as a boy—a gracious disposition, a patience that nothing could disturb, and willing hands ever ready to serve others.

Part III—Stories of Jesus' Ministry

MATTHEW 3:1-4:22; MARK 1:1-20; LUKE 3:1-4:13; JOHN 1:1-4:42

Part IV—Stories of Jesus' Miracles

MATTHEW 4:23-25; 8:5-34; MARK 1:21-2:12; 4:35-5:20; LUKE 4:14-5:11; 7:1-17; 8:22-40; JOHN 4:43-54

PART I

Stories of Jesus as a Baby

(MATTHEW 1:1-2:21; LUKE 1:1-2:40)

STORY 1

The Baby Everybody Wanted

D ID you ever want a baby brother—or a baby sister— to come to your home? If so, you know how eagerly you looked forward to his coming and how happy you were when he arrived. And you loved him because he was yours, your very own.

There was one baby boy, however, whom everybody wanted. For hundreds of years, all over the world, fathers and mothers, brothers and sisters, hoped that this very special baby would come to their home.

For a long time nobody knew just when or where he would be born, so parents everywhere kept wondering, Will he come to our home? And every little girl hoped that she would grow up to be the mother of this baby.

You see, this baby was part of a promise made by God in the Garden of Eden, after Adam and Eve had made their sad mistake. After God had told them that they must leave their beautiful home He said to the serpent who had caused

9

← PAINTING BY HARRY ANDERSON   © 1956, BY REVIEW AND HERALD

As Mary looked upon this lovely babe in her arms, and pondered the far-reaching prophecy of Simeon, she was full of grateful joy and hope that here at last was Israel's Deliverer.

all the trouble, "I will put enmity between thee and the woman, and between thy seed and her seed; it shall bruise thy head, and thou shalt bruise his heel."

This meant that someday a child, or grandchild, or great-grandchild of Eve's would "bruise," or crush, the head of the wicked serpent and undo all the evil he had done. Someday a wonderful baby would be born who would break the power of Satan and regain all that man had lost because of sin.

Eve thought that she would be the mother of this baby. When Cain was born she said, "I have gotten a man from the Lord." But Cain was not the one. He turned out to be a murderer and killed his brother Abel.

After Abel's death Eve had another little boy and called him Seth, meaning "the appointed one." But again she was mistaken. He was not the appointed one.

Of course Eve had baby girls too. And without doubt she told all of them about God's promise. So when each girl grew up and married she hoped that she would be the mother of the wonderful baby who would do all the glorious things God had spoken of. But all were mistaken.

However, they passed on the promise to their little girls, who told it to their little girls, who told it to their little girls, and so on down the years. In this way the hope of a coming Saviour and Deliverer was kept alive from century to century.

That Moses knew about the promise is certain. He said

Genesis 3:15

Deuteronomy 18:15

Numbers 24:17

THE BABY EVERYBODY WANTED

to the children of Israel: "The Lord thy God will raise up unto thee a Prophet from the midst of thee, of thy brethren, like unto me; unto him ye shall hearken."

Balaam knew about it too, for instead of cursing Israel, as Balak wanted him to, he said, "There shall come a Star out of Jacob, and a Sceptre shall rise out of Israel." By this he meant that someone was coming who would be both a light and a king; and people wondered the more when the promised Child would come.

Isaiah 7:14

The prophet Isaiah was more definite. He wrote: "Behold, a virgin shall conceive, and bear a son, and shall call his name Immanuel." Again, "Unto us a child is born, unto us a son is given: and the government shall be upon his shoulder."

After this, many who had lost hope hoped again. Many a little mother, looking down at her precious baby boy, must have asked, Could this be the one? Will my boy grow up to be the great leader whom God has promised to send?

Then the prophet Micah revealed the very place where the Child was to be born. From home to home, and especially from mother to mother, the news spread like wildfire: "But thou, Bethlehem Ephratah, though thou be little among the thousands of Judah, yet out of thee shall he come forth unto me that is to be ruler in Israel."

Micah 5:2

All eyes turned toward Bethlehem. For a little while every mother and child in or near the city became important.

Daniel 9:25

But nothing happened. And as the years rolled by, Micah's prophecy was forgotten. The few who remembered it thought he must have been mistaken.

Then, after the Jews had been taken away into captivity, and everybody was discouraged, another prophet brought thrilling news about the baby. Daniel claimed that the angel Gabriel had told him the exact time when the great Deliverer would appear.

Gabriel, he said, had told him that "from the going forth of the commandment to restore and to build Jerusalem unto the Messiah the Prince shall be seven weeks, and threescore and two weeks."

This was the most definite word yet. From the time that the king of Persia should order the rebuilding of Jerusalem to the coming of "Messiah the Prince" would be sixty-nine weeks (seven plus sixty-two).

Sixty-nine weeks! That's no time at all, people said. He'll be here in less than two years! But others said the weeks must be "prophetic weeks," with each day reckoned as a year.

They were right. And this meant the world had to wait almost another 500 years.

That is a long, long time, and as the years passed, Daniel's words were forgotten and people came to think that the wonderful baby would never come.

Then, when many had given up hope altogether, something happened. The angel Gabriel came again, this time not to a prophet but to a girl. He brought great news from heaven.

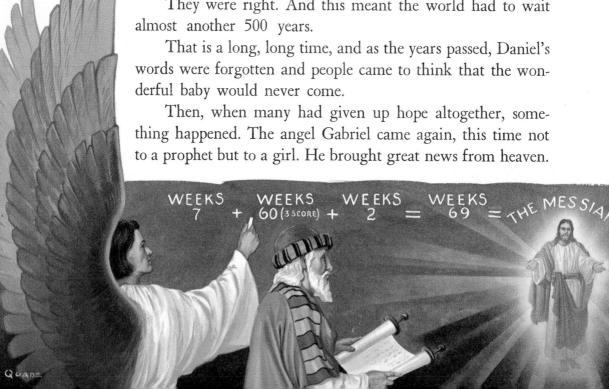

WEEKS 7 + WEEKS 60 (3 SCORE) + WEEKS 2 = WEEKS 69 = THE MESSIAH

STORY 2

Great News From Heaven

A S THE time drew near for the birth of Jesus there must have been great excitement among the angels in heaven. To them this was the most important event of the ages. The Lord, whom they adored, was about to leave the realms of glory to go and dwell on one of the smallest planets He had created. To show how much He loved all His creatures—even those who had rebelled against Him—He was going to wrap Himself up in a little bundle of human flesh and live as a man among men.

How much the angels understood about this miracle of miracles we do not know, but it must have seemed to them the sublimest proof that God is love. So touched were they by this most gracious act that they wanted to tell everybody the wonderful news. How they must have marveled that the people on the earth—except for a very few—did not give a thought to His coming, that nobody was preparing a welcome for Him!

Eagerly they watched as the 483 years of Daniel's prophecy

gradually came to a close. Then, at exactly the right time, not a moment too soon, not a moment too late, God called upon Gabriel to fly swiftly to the earth and find a girl called Mary.

Just why God chose Mary the Bible does not say. But we do know that "the eyes of the Lord run to and fro throughout the whole earth, to shew himself strong in the behalf of them whose heart is perfect toward him." No doubt Mary was the best girl He could find in all the world just then. He had been watching her all her life and knew that her heart was "perfect toward him." He believed He could trust her with this very great honor.

Of course He knew exactly where she lived—the very town, the very street, the very house, the very room. So when Gabriel drew near to Nazareth he made no mistake. A moment later he was beside her.

"Hail, thou that art highly favoured," he said, so kindly and tenderly, "the Lord is with thee: blessed art thou among women."

Mary wondered who her visitor might be and what he meant by these strange words. How could she be "blessed . . . among women"—she, an unknown girl in an out-of-the-way village like Nazareth!

Seeing how frightened she was, Gabriel spoke more gently still. "Fear not, Mary," he said, "for thou hast found favour with God. And, behold, thou shalt conceive in thy womb, and bring forth a son, and shalt call his name Jesus.

"He shall be great, and shall be called the Son of the Highest: and the Lord God shall give unto him the throne

15

← PAINTING BY RUSSELL HARLAN   © 1956, BY REVIEW AND HERALD

Gabriel made the astonishing announcement: "Fear not, Mary: for thou hast found favour with God. And, behold, thou shalt . . . bring forth a son, and shalt call his name Jesus."

of his father David: and he shall reign over the house of Jacob for ever; and of his kingdom there shall be no end."

To Mary this didn't seem possible. Her son to be a king! To sit on David's throne! To reign forever! Oh, no! She must be dreaming. Anyway, it couldn't happen, because she wasn't married. She was just betrothed to Joseph, that was all, and she told Gabriel so, in case he didn't know it.

Of course Gabriel knew it, and he was ready with his answer. If Mary were willing, he said, something very, very wonderful would happen to her. In perhaps the most beautiful words to be found in all the Bible, he said to her: "The Holy Ghost shall come upon thee, and the power of the Highest shall overshadow thee: therefore also that holy thing which shall be born of thee shall be called the Son of God."

Seeing that Mary still doubted, he told her a secret that must have surprised her very much: "Behold, thy cousin Elisabeth, she hath also conceived a son in her old age: and this is the sixth month with her, who was called barren."

"Elisabeth having a baby!" I can hear Mary whispering to herself. "Not Elisabeth! And how does this stranger know that it's going to be a boy?"

Gabriel smiled. "With God nothing shall be impossible," he said.

Mary bowed her head. "Behold the handmaid of the Lord," she said, "be it unto me according to thy word."

A moment later Gabriel vanished, and Mary was left alone wondering what it all meant and what was going to happen to her.

16

Like many another God-fearing girl in Israel she had
thought how honored she would be if she could be the mother
of the wonderful baby so many people had been expecting for
hundreds and hundreds of years, but she had never dared to
hope it might be so. And now somebody—it must have been
an angel—had told her that this baby was going to be hers—
HERS! She was going to be the mother of the Messiah. Her
son would be the great Deliverer of her people, the One of
whom patriarchs and prophets had spoken from the dawn of
time. Yes! And He would be called "the Son of the Highest"
and "the Son of God."

It was too wonderful to be real, too good to be true. Yet
it was real and it was true.

The wonderful baby was on His way.

STORY 3

Two Happy Mothers

"ELISABETH!"

"Mary!"

Surprise and happiness were in 'their eager greeting.

Though close relatives, they had not met for some time. Travel was difficult in those days. There were no cars, of course. One had to go from place to place on donkeyback or on foot, or not at all.

So anxious was Mary to find out whether the mysterious stranger had told the truth about Elisabeth that she had gone all the way "into the hill country with haste, into a city of Juda." When she found Elisabeth and her husband Zacharias there, she realized at once that Gabriel had made no mistake.

What a story Elisabeth had to tell! She said that for a long time she and her husband had been praying that they might have a baby, but none had come. Then one day, about six months before, when Zacharias was busy in the Temple— for he was a priest—an angel had appeared to him and said,

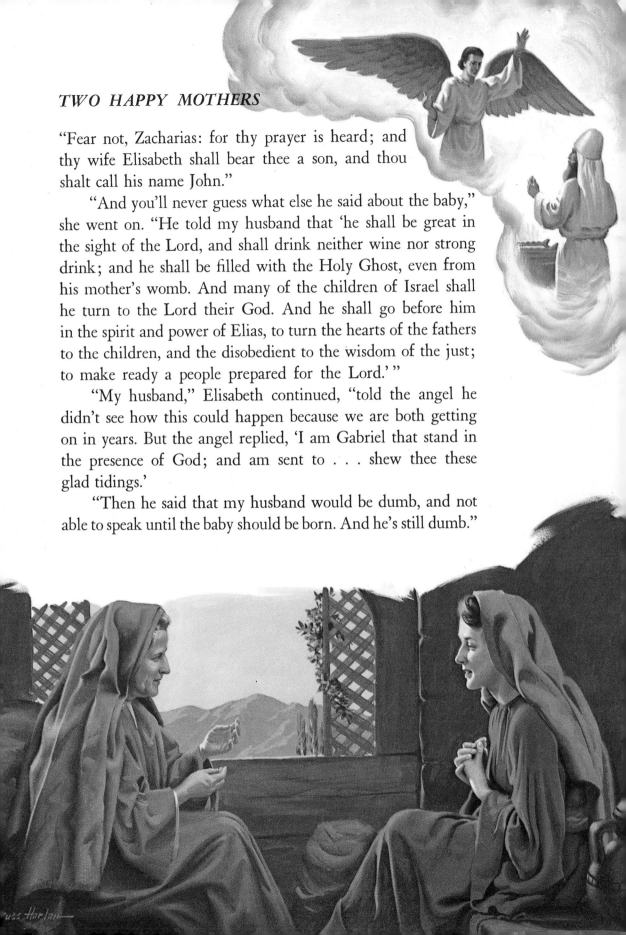

TWO HAPPY MOTHERS

"Fear not, Zacharias: for thy prayer is heard; and thy wife Elisabeth shall bear thee a son, and thou shalt call his name John."

"And you'll never guess what else he said about the baby," she went on. "He told my husband that 'he shall be great in the sight of the Lord, and shall drink neither wine nor strong drink; and he shall be filled with the Holy Ghost, even from his mother's womb. And many of the children of Israel shall he turn to the Lord their God. And he shall go before him in the spirit and power of Elias, to turn the hearts of the fathers to the children, and the disobedient to the wisdom of the just; to make ready a people prepared for the Lord.'"

"My husband," Elisabeth continued, "told the angel he didn't see how this could happen because we are both getting on in years. But the angel replied, 'I am Gabriel that stand in the presence of God; and am sent to . . . shew thee these glad tidings.'

"Then he said that my husband would be dumb, and not able to speak until the baby should be born. And he's still dumb."

Then Mary told *her* story, sure now that it was Gabriel who had spoken to her.

Elisabeth listened with growing surprise. Suddenly she caught the full meaning of Gabriel's message. "Blessed art thou among women," she said to Mary. "And whence is this to me, that the mother of my Lord should come to me?"

Then the Holy Spirit came upon Mary, and she spoke these beautiful words of praise to the One who had honored her so greatly:

"My soul doth magnify the Lord, and my spirit hath rejoiced in God my Saviour. For he hath regarded the low estate of his handmaiden: for, behold, from henceforth all generations shall call me blessed.

"For he that is mighty hath done to me great things; and holy is his name. And his mercy is on them that fear him from generation to generation.

"He hath shewed strength with his arm; he hath scattered the proud in the imagination of their hearts. He hath put down the mighty from their seats, and exalted them of low degree.

"He hath filled the hungry with good things; and the rich he hath sent empty away.

"He hath holpen his servant Israel, in remembrance of his mercy; as he spake to our fathers, to Abraham, and to his seed for ever."

Mary stayed in the home of

20

Zacharias for three months, until it was time for Elisabeth's baby to be born.

There was quite a fuss then about naming the baby. Elisabeth said he was to be called John, but the neighbors insisted his name should be Zacharias, after his father. When they asked Zacharias, he still couldn't speak, but he made signs that he wanted to say something. They brought him writing material and this is what he wrote: "His name is John."

At once his dumbness left him and "he spake, and praised God." Then he told the neighbors all that had happened from the day Gabriel spoke to him in the Temple. They were amazed and said to one another, "What manner of child shall this be!"

Zacharias, now filled with the Holy Spirit, went on, "Blessed be the Lord God of Israel; for he hath visited and redeemed his people, and hath raised up an horn of salvation for us in the house of his servant David; as he spake by the mouth of his holy prophets, which have been since the world began: that we should be saved from our enemies, and from the hand of all that hate us; to perform the mercy promised to our fathers, and to remember his holy covenant; the oath which he sware to our father Abraham, that he would grant unto us, that we being delivered out of the hand of our enemies might serve him without fear, in holiness and righteousness before him, all the days of our life.

"And thou child," he said, looking down lovingly at little John, "shalt be called the prophet of the Highest: for thou shalt go before the face of the Lord to prepare his ways; to give knowledge of salvation unto his people by the remission of their sins, through the tender mercy of our God; whereby the dayspring from on high hath visited us, to give light to them that sit in darkness and in the shadow of death, to guide our feet into the way of peace."

I can almost feel the hush that came over the little group of people gathered round baby John as they listened to Zacharias. I think they sensed that a great moment in history had arrived.

It had. Heaven was drawing very near to earth. God had called for two baby boys. One was born, the other was on His way. One was to be "the prophet of the Highest," the other "the Son of the Highest." What a stir they would make when they grew up!

STORY 4

The Wonderful Name

≈≈≈≈≈≈≈≈≈≈≈≈

AFTER the birth of John, Mary returned to Nazareth, where Joseph was waiting eagerly for her return.

What a story she had to tell him! She must have been full of it. There was Gabriel's visit to Zacharias; Elisabeth's surprise at getting a baby; how John got his name; and finally Gabriel's strange and thrilling message to herself.

As Joseph listened to this part of her story he became very worried. He didn't know what to make of it. It was all so unusual that he could hardly believe it. Was Mary telling him the truth? Had she really seen an angel? Would her baby be the Son of God and the king of Israel? How strange!

But God knew his thoughts, and that very night He sent Gabriel to speak to him in a dream. Gabriel told him that he need not worry. What had happened to Mary was according to God's plan. What's more, he said, "She shall bring forth a son, and thou shalt call his name Jesus: for he shall save his people from their sins."

23

When Joseph awoke next morning I am sure he told Mary all about his dream. Indeed, I can almost hear him saying, Gabriel has spoken to me too. He told me that your story is true, and he wants me to call the baby 'Jesus.'"

"He told me the same," Mary may well have said.

"But there's nobody in our family by that name."

"I know. Surely it must have some special meaning."

"It does; it means 'Saviour.' This Child, Gabriel said, is to save His people from their sins."

I am sure neither Joseph nor Mary understood fully what Gabriel meant. Not then. Like the rest of the people of Israel they hoped someone would come to save them from the Romans—from the cruelty of their soldiers and the meanness of their tax collectors. But they never thought that such a person would save them from their *sins*. How would that help? Yet God knew that if this should happen, all Israel's other troubles would come to an end.

In these wonderful words Gabriel tried to tell Joseph and Mary the most precious secret ever told. He wanted them to be the first to know that this baby boy who was coming to them was the very one who, as God had promised, would break the power of Satan. This precious child would grow up to be the Saviour of the world. He would help people to stop doing wrong. He would make them good and true and noble. And one day He would lead them back to long-lost Eden and restore everything that Satan took away.

"Thou shalt call his name Jesus," said Gabriel, so that every time anyone should call Him by this name they would think of Him as a Saviour and remember that He is able and willing to save them from the worst of sins.

"Thou shalt call his name Jesus," that people of all nations should think of Him as One who would help them in every time of need.

"Thou shalt call his name Jesus," that hope might come to the hopeless and joy to the sad, to the ends of the earth and the end of time.

No wonder the prophet Isaiah said that "his name shall be called Wonderful." It is wonderful—the most wonderful name anyone ever was given.

"Thou shalt call his name Jesus: for he shall save his people from their sins."

More than nineteen hundred years have passed since Gabriel spoke these words to Joseph, but they mean as much and more today. They glow more brightly every passing day. Their glorious message is for you, for me, for everybody. He *can* save us and He *will* save us if we will let Him. And He will save us from *all* our sins.

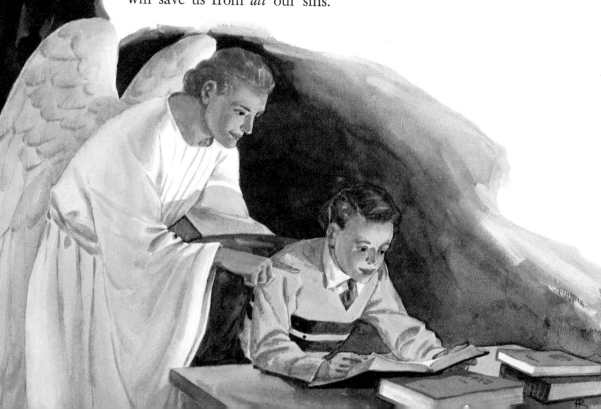

STORY 5

Just in Time!

SLOWLY the weeks passed as Mary looked forward to the day when her wonderful baby would be born. I am sure she prayed over and over again that God would make her the best little mother that ever was. She wanted so much to be worthy of the great honor He had shown her.

Then one morning there was wild excitement in the sleepy little village of Nazareth. Roman soldiers came galloping into the market place. They said they had orders from the emperor in Rome.

Soon everybody was running toward them, eager to find out what was going on. Boys and girls pushed through the gathering crowd to get a better view of the splendid uniforms the soldiers were wearing.

"This is a decree from Caesar Augustus," cried an officer, unrolling a scroll, which he began to read. "Every citizen is to make his way at once to his home town to be registered."

As the people listened, their hearts sank. They guessed

this was part of a new plan to get more taxes out of them. But there was nothing they could do about it. They had to obey.

Joseph was much upset. Because he was "of the house of David" his home town was Bethlehem, eighty miles or so away. The last thing he wanted to do just now was to take Mary all that way. Her baby was due any time, and Joseph was afraid something might go wrong.

Today, of course, one can travel from Nazareth to Bethlehem by car in a couple of hours, but in those days it meant a long, tiring journey on donkeyback over steep mountain trails and rough, rutted roads. Three or four miles an hour was top speed, which meant a four-day trip at least, with no nice auto courts to stay in at night.

Joseph and Mary must have talked it over very seriously. Should they stay in Nazareth and risk trouble with the Romans, or should they try to get to Bethlehem in time, trusting God to watch over them on the way?

JUST IN TIME!

They decided to go to Bethlehem. Mary was lifted carefully onto a donkey, and Joseph either walked beside her or rode another animal.

It was rough going, and no doubt many a time Joseph asked, "Are you all right, Mary? Are you sure?"

Many a time, too, he must have wished that the donkey would move faster. Never, it seemed, had it gone so slowly. And never had there been so much traffic. So many people were on their way to register as the Romans had bidden them.

But if Joseph was worried, his concern was nothing compared to that of the watching angels. Better than anybody on earth they knew that the wonderful baby was to be born in Bethlehem, not in Nazareth, or Jerusalem, or somewhere in between. God had said so, through the prophet Micah. And so, somehow, it must surely happen. But here was Mary on donkeyback, miles away from Bethlehem and time running out fast. Would she make it?

Oh, that donkey! Why wouldn't it go faster! How they must have wanted to get behind it and push!

Mile after weary mile the two tired people traveled. At night they rested as best they could, moving on next morning at break of day.

Two days passed. Three days.

"Are you all right, Mary?"

"I think so—I hope so. Is there much farther to go?"

"Not far. It won't be long now."

Evening was drawing on again as they slowly passed Jerusalem, where the traffic was worse than ever. They had only six miles to go now.

Another hour went by. Darkness was falling. Soon pinpoints of light could be seen in the distance.

"Bethlehem!" cried Joseph.

"Thank God!" murmured Mary. "Bethlehem!"

They had made it—just in time.

STORY 6

"No Vacancy"

HAVE you ever been traveling late at night and found a "No Vacancy" sign on every auto court and motel? If so, you know how very tired it made you feel. The thought that there was no place to rest, nowhere to go, seemed just too much to take, didn't it?

Imagine then how poor Joseph and Mary felt when they reached the only inn in town and found it full to overflowing. "There was no room for them in the inn."

It wasn't the innkeeper's fault. He couldn't help it. Probably he was beside himself trying to find food, let alone rooms, for all the people crowding into the city to obey the decree of Caesar Augustus.

When he saw Mary, and guessed what was the matter, I am sure he was sorry for her. Who would not have been? But what could he do? When a hotel is full it's full, that's all.

Of course, if the innkeeper had known all Mary knew— that it was the Messiah Himself who was to be born that night

—he would have found a place for her somewhere, even if he had had to give up his own room. And here he missed a great blessing. What a story he would have had to tell for the rest of his life! How famous his inn would have become! People would have talked of his good fortune to the end of time.

By failing to do the best he could for a poor, needy girl he lost a great opportunity. Jesus may well say to him someday, "Inasmuch as ye did it not to one of the least of these, ye did it not to me." How careful we should be when someone comes to us in need!

But in the hurry and bustle of the moment the innkeeper did not think of all this. Instead, he offered his stable.

"The stable!" said Joseph. "Is that all you have?"

"At least it's shelter, and better than nothing."

The stable!

As Mary heard the word her heart sank. All day she had longed for a comfortable place to rest. Now there was nothing but a stable! Maybe she cried. I am sure she thought of what Gabriel had said to her: "He shall be great, and shall be called the Son of the Highest: and the Lord God shall give unto him the throne of his father David: and he shall reign over the house of Jacob for ever; and of his kingdom there shall be no end."

Could she have been mistaken? she wondered. If what Gabriel had said was true why was there nothing ready for her baby? Surely "the Son of the Highest" should not be born in a smelly old stable!

A door creaked in the darkness. Joseph went ahead with a lantern. A cow mooed. A horse neighed. A rooster crowed.

"This way," said Joseph. "There's some clean straw over here." Peering through the gloom, Mary saw an empty manger, half filled with hay for the cows to eat.

"This will do for the baby," she said.

A manger! Yes, it would do. But what a strange place for the "Son of the Highest" to lie.

Strange indeed! He could not have chosen a humbler place for His coming into the world. Perhaps it was because He wanted the humblest and the poorest to know that He loved them and that He was willing to share their lot.

No red carpet was spread for Him when He came from heaven to earth. There was only the straw on a muddy floor.

No fine linen, no downy quilt, was provided for His bed, only the fragrant hay.

No trumpets blared a welcome when He came. There was no sound at all save the mooing of cows, the neighing of horses, the braying of donkeys, the barking of dogs, as the dumb creatures of His creation tried their best to say, "We're glad you've come to see us."

Then, suddenly, it happened. The wonderful baby was born. And they called Him Jesus.

Nobody was there save Joseph and Mary and the angels. Yet it was the most wonderful event in history. All heaven had waited thousands of years for this moment. Patriarchs and prophets had longed for it since the dawn of time. Yet nobody was there. Nobody knew. Nobody cared.

In His infinite love the Son of God had stepped from heaven to earth to take on "the likeness of man" and "the form of a servant" that He might be our Saviour and Redeemer; and here He was, lying in a manger. Here was the all-powerful Lord of creation weak and helpless as a little child; here was the all-wise King Eternal unable to speak a single word; here was the Source of all life dependent for food upon a girl.

This was indeed "love divine, all love excelling, joy of heaven, to earth come down."

Don't you wish you could have been there to welcome Him? Just to say, "Thank you, dear Lord," for such love as this?

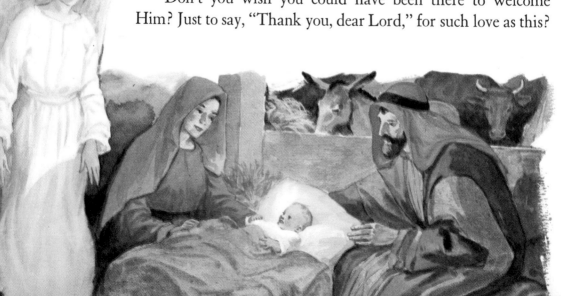

STORY 7

Night of Nights

≈≈≈≈≈≈≈≈≈≈≈≈≈

SUPPOSE you had been living in Bethlehem that night when Jesus was born. What would you have seen and heard?

Imagine for a moment you are there. You and your brother. It is a warm night, so you are lying on a bed on the roof of a flat-topped house. The rest of the family is asleep, but you are awake, looking up at the sky, trying to count the stars.

"I never saw so many people in our town," you say.

"I wonder how long they will stay?" says your brother.

"Till the taxing is over, I suppose."

There is silence for a moment.

"I've been wondering," you say.

"Wondering what?"

"About what father has been telling us lately. You know, about the Messiah's coming. He says the time is nearly up and the old prophecies must be fulfilled soon."

"Isn't He to come to Bethlehem?"

35

"Yes. He's to be born here. The prophet Micah says so. I wonder when?"

There is a pause. Then a cry.

"Look at that! Up there in the sky!"

"What? Where?"

"The light! The beautiful light. What can it be?"

"Looks like a star. It's right over the inn. No, it isn't. It's over the stable behind the inn. What can be happening? Let's go and see! Quietly now. Don't wake everybody!"

Silently you both creep downstairs, cross the road, and walk toward the inn. Suddenly you stop, for the light seems to have moved outside the town.

You run past the guards at the gates and across the fields to the place where the shepherds keep their sheep at night.

You see a group of men standing open-mouthed as a glorious being talks to them.

Can this be the Messiah? you wonder. Surely not. Then it must be an angel! You hear him saying, "Fear not: for, behold, I bring you good tidings of great joy, which shall be to all people. For unto you is born this day in the city of David a Saviour, which is Christ the Lord."

"Did you hear that?" you ask. "He says Messiah is here, that He has just been born!"

"Sh-sh! Listen. The angel is speaking again."

"And this shall be a sign unto you," the angel says. "Ye shall find the babe wrapped in swaddling clothes, lying in a manger."

Suddenly you see a perfectly marvelous sight. Right before your eyes appears a multitude of shining angels, thousands upon thousands of them, all singing together, "Glory to God in the highest, and on earth peace, good will toward men."

The whole heavens are flooded with light. Everywhere it is as bright as day. You can see the rugged mountains all around, the awe-struck shepherds, the trembling sheep, and every building in Bethlehem. Oh, yes, and the angels. So many angels, all singing their loudest as though they had been waiting ages and ages to sing this song.

38

NIGHT OF NIGHTS

"Glory to God! Glory to God! Glory to God in the highest!" The majestic music seems to roll clear round the world and out toward the stars, "Glory to God in the highest!"

Then, more gently, "On earth peace, good will toward men." How tenderly and hopefully they sing these closing words of their lovely hymn of praise! It is as if they long to see men everywhere welcome their Saviour with open arms and make Him the Lord of their lives.

As suddenly as they came, the angels disappear. Darkness settles again over the fields and hills. You watch the shepherds to see what they will do. You hear them say, "Let us now go even unto Bethlehem, and see this thing which is come to pass, which the Lord hath made known unto us."

"Let's go at once!" they all cry, and you see them hurrying off toward the city gate, stumbling over rocks and briers in their haste, but getting up and hurrying on, eager to tell somebody the great news they have heard.

You run behind them to see where they will go.

They pass a sleepy-eyed citizen near the inn.

"Was a baby born around here tonight?" a shepherd asks.

"Yes, down there in the stable."

They run on. It is still dark, though dawn is on the way. A dim light comes through cracks in the door.

And what is that? A baby's cry! This must be the place. They push open the door and peer in. You are right behind them.

At the far end a man is standing. Beside him is a young woman resting on a pile of straw. Beside her, in a manger, is a baby, wrapped in swaddling clothes.

Surely this must be the baby the angel spoke about. And if so, He must be the promised Saviour, Christ the Lord!

Reverently the shepherds enter the stable. Joseph and Mary look up startled, wondering what these strange, rough men are doing here at this time of night. Have they come to turn them out?

No indeed! They have come to see the baby.

One of the shepherds begins to explain. They were in the field, he says, keeping watch over their flocks by night, when all of a sudden they saw an angel, who told them that this very night the Messiah would be born and they would find Him lying in a manger.

Mary's eyes glow. She understands. And she is glad. Now she is sure God has not forgotten her. He knows where the baby is, even though He is lying in a manger.

Over and over again the shepherds tell their story, with

first one, then another, breaking in to add some fresh detail about what happened that night. And all the while they keep looking down at the baby and saying how lovely He is.

As it dawns upon them ever more clearly that this is indeed the long-promised Messiah, the Son of the living God, they kneel beside the manger and worship Him, the first in all the world to do so.

By-and-by they bid good-by to Joseph and Mary and go on their way. As they do so the sun is coming up over the mountains. A new day is dawning for Bethlehem and the world.

People are just waking up and getting breakfast. Some are tending their animals. They look at the shepherds in astonishment, for with faces aglow these roughly dressed men are "glorifying and praising God" right in the main street! Eagerly they are stopping passers-by and telling them about the marvelous things they saw and heard that night.

"You mean you saw angels?" somebody says to them. "Angels here in Bethlehem?"

"Yes, indeed, a multitude of the heavenly host, praising God and saying——"

"Impossible!"

"But we did. They told us Messiah was born."

"Messiah born here last night! Oh, no. That couldn't be."

"Yes, indeed. It's true! He's in the stable over there behind the inn."

"And all they that heard it wondered at those things that were told them by the shepherds."

Some believed their story; others did not. Some went to the stable to see the Christ Child. Others didn't bother. They let the greatest event of the ages go right past them without a thought. They busied themselves with their daily chores—washing dishes, cleaning house, feeding animals, making money—while the very one they said they wanted so much was right in their midst. How careful we should be lest we let ourselves get so busy that we do not realize when Jesus is near!

Of those who went to the stable that morning, some saw just another baby, and some saw God. It has been that way ever since. It is that way still. As you look at Him today, whom do *you* see?

STORY 8

This Is the One!

IF YOU could have been in the Temple at Jerusalem about six weeks after Jesus was born you would have seen a very old man looking eagerly at the babies that mothers and fathers were bringing to the priests for dedication.

His name was Simeon, and he had been interested in babies for a long time now. Mothers loved the way he looked at their children as though he really cared about them. They thought he must be a very kindhearted old man, and he was.

But he was more than just a kindly old grandfather. He was a scholar, and knew the Holy Scriptures from Genesis to Malachi. For years and years he had been looking for "the consolation of Israel." He had studied all the prophecies about the Messiah and was sure in his heart that the time had come for Him to appear. What's more, the Lord had told him that he would not die until he had seen the Child of promise.

That's why he looked so keenly at every baby brought to the Temple. Of course, the parents didn't know what was going on in his mind, but he was asking himself all the time, Could this be the one? Or this? Or this?

Every day mothers and fathers would be there with their new-born children to dedicate them to God and offer thank offerings, and Simeon never tired of talking with them and looking at their babies. Day after day he searched for the One he longed to see.

One day as he entered the Temple he noticed two poorly dressed people who had come to dedicate their little son. That they were Galileans he could see by their garments. That they were poor was clear from the fact that they were carrying two birds in a cage as their offering. "A pair of turtledoves, or two young pigeons" was the gift that only the poorest people were supposed to bring.

Simeon had never seen these people before, but there was something about them that interested him very much, particularly the young woman with the sweet, gentle face. Here, he felt sure, was one who loved the Lord. There was no doubt about that.

He looked down at the child and suddenly his heart stirred.

Somehow it came to him, all of a sudden. It was as though the voice of God had spoken to him saying, "This is the Messiah! This is the One for whom you have been looking so long!"

Tears of happiness rolled down the old man's cheeks as, taking the precious baby and holding Him close, he said, "Lord, now lettest thou thy servant depart in peace, according to thy word: for mine eyes have seen thy salvation, which thou hast prepared before the face of all people; a light to

44

lighten the Gentiles, and the glory of thy people Israel."

Joseph and Mary looked on, amazed. The Bible says they marveled at the things Simeon was saying about their child. And Mary may well have said to herself, "How does he know? Did Gabriel tell him too?"

Then the old man turned to Joseph and Mary and blessed them. Looking into Mary's eager, upturned face, he spoke

45

directly to her, saying, "Behold, this child is set for the fall and rising again of many in Israel; and for a sign which shall be spoken against; (yea, a sword shall pierce through thy own soul also,) that the thoughts of many hearts may be revealed."

Mary wondered what he meant. What strange destiny was ahead of her precious little Jesus? How would He cause people to fall and rise again? And what was this about a sword piercing her soul? Was not her child to become King of Israel? How then could there be any suffering? Some day she would understand, but not now.

Hardly had she time to think about Simeon's strange words before an elderly woman came hurrying over to them. Her name was Anna. She was eighty-four years old, and a prophetess. All excited, she took one look at Mary and her baby, and began to thank God aloud that He had sent the Messiah at last. People around heard her and came to see what was going on. Eagerly Anna told her story and "spake of him to all them that looked for redemption in Jerusalem."

Some believed her; others doubted; but most just said, "What a lovely baby!" and went on their way without giving the matter another thought.

But to Mary the words of Simeon and Anna meant a great deal. Now she was more sure than ever that her baby was indeed the Messiah, the Child of promise and prophecy.

46

STORY 9

Strangers From the East

≈≈≈≈≈≈≈≈≈≈≈≈≈≈

HOW many people saw the wondrous light in the sky when the angels came to Bethlehem to rejoice over the birth of Jesus nobody will ever know. But that it was seen hundreds of miles away there is no doubt.

Far to the east of Palestine, possibly in Arabia, or Persia, a little group of men not only saw the light but were convinced it had some special meaning.

How old they were the Bible does not say, but we know they were wise and learned. Certainly they knew the Hebrew Scriptures well, for they were sure that the time had come for the king of Israel to appear. They must have studied the prophecies of Daniel, Moses, Isaiah, and others. They had worked out the seventy-week prophecy better than the leaders of Israel had done, and had taken literally the promise "there shall come a Star out of Jacob."

When they saw the strange light they said to themselves, "This must be what we have been expecting." Then they set

47

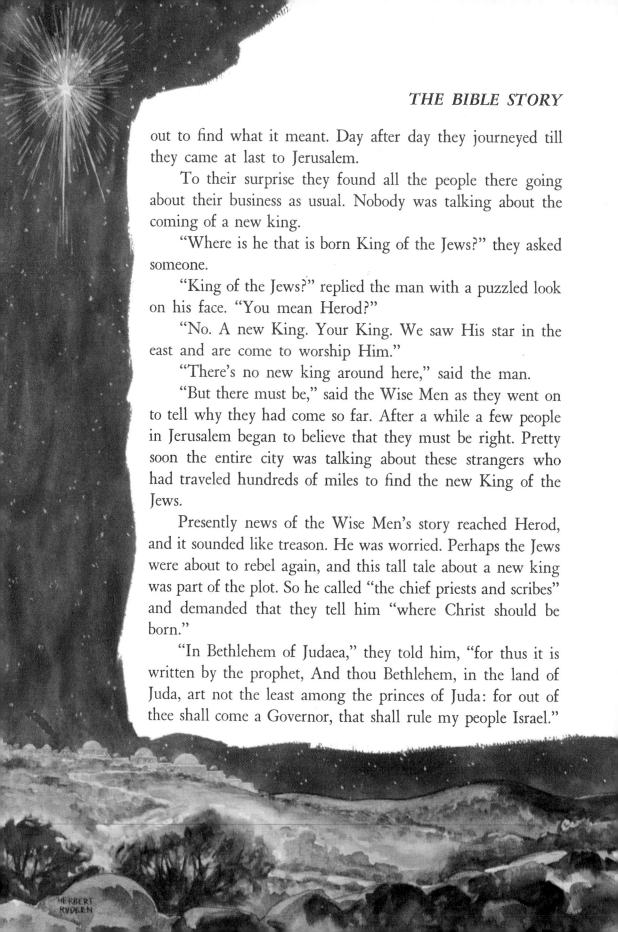

out to find what it meant. Day after day they journeyed till they came at last to Jerusalem.

To their surprise they found all the people there going about their business as usual. Nobody was talking about the coming of a new king.

"Where is he that is born King of the Jews?" they asked someone.

"King of the Jews?" replied the man with a puzzled look on his face. "You mean Herod?"

"No. A new King. Your King. We saw His star in the east and are come to worship Him."

"There's no new king around here," said the man.

"But there must be," said the Wise Men as they went on to tell why they had come so far. After a while a few people in Jerusalem began to believe that they must be right. Pretty soon the entire city was talking about these strangers who had traveled hundreds of miles to find the new King of the Jews.

Presently news of the Wise Men's story reached Herod, and it sounded like treason. He was worried. Perhaps the Jews were about to rebel again, and this tall tale about a new king was part of the plot. So he called "the chief priests and scribes" and demanded that they tell him "where Christ should be born."

"In Bethlehem of Judaea," they told him, "for thus it is written by the prophet, And thou Bethlehem, in the land of Juda, art not the least among the princes of Juda: for out of thee shall come a Governor, that shall rule my people Israel."

STRANGERS FROM THE EAST

Somehow, from the way the priests and scribes talked, Herod felt sure that *they* did not believe that any new king had been born. So far as they were concerned their "governor" might not appear in Bethlehem for hundreds of years yet. But he was troubled by the rumor that the Wise Men from the East had started. Was there anything to it? He would find out.

Herod sent for the Wise Men. They were still in town and came gladly. He treated them graciously, and asked them to tell him exactly what they had told so many others. They did; and Herod listened with great interest. Then he asked, "When did you first see this star?"

They told him.

"And how long have you been on your way?"

They told him that too.

"Do you think that this new king is to be born in Bethlehem?"

"Certainly."

"And you believe he is already born?"

"The prophecies suggest it."

"H'm. I'll tell you what," said Herod. "You go to Bethlehem and find this child. Then send me word, and I will come and worship him also."

The Wise Men thanked the king and left. This was the best thing that had happened to them since they arrived in Jerusalem. The great King Herod was now going to help them in their search!

With lighter hearts they set out for Bethlehem. Then they saw something that filled them with "exceeding great joy." There, in the sky above the little town, they saw the star again, the very one they had seen in the east many weeks ago. I can almost hear them saying to one another, "Look! There it is again!"

Now they urged their camels forward with new eagerness, sure that their search was almost at an end.

As they clattered through the gates of David's city, people looked up and wondered who these wealthy-looking strangers might be. But the taxing had brought so many people to town, both rich and poor, that they took no special notice of them.

At last the three Wise Men came to the house where Joseph and Mary were now staying. As they entered "they saw the young child with Mary his mother, and fell down and worshipped him."

What a sight that must have been as these three Wise Men, clad in their rich garments, bent low before the Baby Jesus!

Imagine what Mary must have thought! Can't you see her eyes growing wide with amazement as the strangers opened up bags and boxes of various kinds and brought out treasures such as she had never seen before? Gold, frankincense, and myrrh were gifts fit for a king, and here they were being poured out before her little boy! I think she must have cried in joy and gratitude.

"Thank you! Thank you!" I can hear her saying. "How kind of you to come so far and give us so much!"

Then they left and vanished into history. Nobody knows what happened to them. Yet that one gracious deed of theirs will live forever.

STORY 10

Narrow Escape

KING HEROD waited and waited for the Wise Men to return. But they never came.

They had planned to go home through Jerusalem, for they thought the king really wanted to find the Child and worship Him, as he had said. But the very night after they had visited Joseph and Mary, God warned them in a dream not to return to Herod. So "they departed into their own country another way."

For a while Herod was not worried. He had not believed their story about seeing a strange star in the sky, and he chuckled as he recalled sending them to Bethlehem to find a baby who was to be king of the Jews. Such a wild-goose chase! he had thought. There couldn't be any such child.

But after several days had passed and no word had reached him from the strangers, he decided to find out what they were doing. So he sent messengers to Bethlehem to check on them. Then he learned that they had secretly left the city

53

long since and gone home without saying a word to anybody.

Now he was angry. How dared they go off like this! Why hadn't they told him the result of their search, as they had promised? He began to be suspicious. Perhaps they *had* found the child they were looking for and wanted to keep the secret to themselves. Yes! That was it! They must be parties to a plot to set up a new king of Israel!

"All right!" the cruel king said to himself. "I'll fix that. No new king will come out of Bethlehem if I have anything to do with it."

In his rage he ordered a company of soldiers to go to Bethlehem and kill every child of two years old and younger. They were to do a thorough job. Not a single baby was to be spared.

It was a terribly wicked thing to do, and even the hardened soldiers must have hated doing it. Yet what could they do but obey? Sick at heart, but with swords sharpened, they set out for the doomed city.

But even as they clattered out of the gate of Jerusalem all heaven moved into action to save the Baby Jesus. Herod had reckoned without God's secret service. Scarcely had his order been heard by the watching angels than one was sent posthaste to the house where Joseph and Mary were staying.

It was night, and they were both asleep.

"Get up!" the angel said to Joseph. "Quickly! Take the young Child, and flee into Egypt. Stay there till I tell you. Herod is planning to destroy the Child."

Joseph awoke, sensing danger near.
"Mary!" he cried. "Wake up!"
Mary stirred in her sleep.
"What's the matter?" she asked.
"We must leave at once!"
"Why?"
"Herod wants to kill the baby. An angel just told me."
"But why?"
"I don't know."
Mary rose to her feet, anxiety showing on her face.
"But where can we go?"
"To Egypt. He said we would be safe there."
Quickly they dressed and packed their things, carefully
hiding the treasures the Wise Men had given them.

Soon their donkey was loaded and they were on their way.

It was a narrow escape. They had not gone far when Herod's soldiers arrived and began breaking into people's homes. Heartlessly they tore the children from their mother's arms and killed them.

Then it was that Jeremiah's prophecy came true: "In Rama was there a voice heard, lamentation, and weeping, and great mourning, Rachel weeping for her children, and would not be comforted, because they are not."

What a dreadful night that was! So many children murdered, so many homes left desolate!

Perhaps upon the ears of the Baby Jesus—now well on His way to safety—fell the cries of the mothers and babes of Bethlehem. He could not help them now, but some day He would be the comforter of Israel, the deliverer of all who should trust in Him.

PART II

Stories of Jesus' Boyhood

(LUKE 2:41-52)

STORY 1

Journey to Egypt

SLOWLY, very slowly, Joseph and Mary made their way southward with their precious baby. It was a long, tiresome journey, for much of the road lay through a dry, sandy desert, where there were no comfortable places for anybody to rest.

It isn't more than a hundred miles from Bethlehem to the border of Egypt, and today you could travel that distance in a couple of hours; but in those days it meant several days' hard traveling.

Poor Mary! How she must have wondered why all this should have happened to her. Why should Herod want to kill her baby? And if little Jesus was indeed the Son of the Highest, as Gabriel had told her, why couldn't she have a home in which to care for Him? Why did she have to wander about like this, owning nothing in the world save the few things tied on the donkey's back?

To all her questions she could find no answer, not then.

Joseph received warning to flee into Egypt with Mary and Jesus to escape the cruelty of Herod. Their way paid by the Magi's gifts, they set out by night to live among strangers.

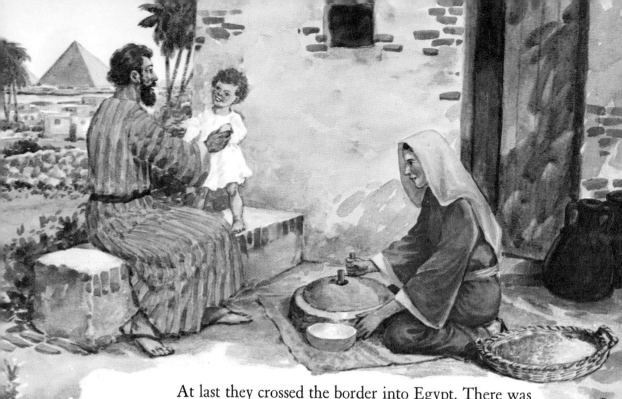

At last they crossed the border into Egypt. There was not much difference in the scenery—just more sand, more desert —but oh, what a relief to know that they were safe from Herod's soldiers at last!

How far they went into Egypt the Bible does not say; but we can be sure that they passed the pyramids, which Abraham had seen when he came this way. And they must have walked by the Nile, where Moses was laid in the bulrushes when he was a baby.

Just where they lived in Egypt, or how long they stayed there, nobody knows. It could be that Joseph got work as a carpenter to help pay expenses, while Mary stayed in some humble home and cared tenderly for her baby.

One night, when Jesus was still a very little boy the angel of the Lord came again to Joseph, this time with good news.

60

JOURNEY TO EGYPT

King Herod was dead, he said, and it was now safe for them to return to Palestine.

"Arise," said the angel, "and take the young child and his mother, and go into the land of Israel: for they are dead which sought the young child's life."

When Joseph told Mary what the angel had said, I can imagine she wept for joy at the thought of going home. True, God had been good to them in Egypt. What with the money Joseph had been able to earn, and the gold that the Wise Men had given them, they had been able to live comfortably: but always they had felt they were strangers in a strange land. Never a day had passed but they had felt the tug of their homeland.

Now they could go back and see their friends and loved ones again. It was too good to be true!

Packing up once more, they prepared to leave the land that had given them shelter in their time of need. One bright morning they set out northward, following—at least part of the way—much the same route that the Israelites traveled when Moses led them out of Egypt to Canaan.

Did you ever wonder what Jesus thought about it all? He had come into Egypt in His mother's arms but He left it on His own sturdy little legs. Of course, He was too little to walk very far, and no doubt Joseph had to lift Him up on the donkey beside Mary every now and then to give Him a rest; but like every other healthy little boy He was eager to act grown-up as much as possible.

He was just beginning to talk too, and probably asked

an endless stream of questions. I can almost hear Him saying,

"What's that animal, Mamma? That one with the big hump on his back?"

"That's a camel, dear."

"And that one with the pointy things on its head?"

"That's an ox; and the pointy things are its horns."

"And what's that funny house over there?"

"That isn't a house, dear. It's a place where the Egyptians buried one of their kings, long, long ago. They call it a pyramid."

"And who's that lady lying down in front of the pyramid? She seems to be smiling at me."

"Oh, that's a very old statue cut out of rock. It's called the Sphinx."

So He chattered on, asking questions and questions and still more questions about everything He saw. Patiently Mary answered them all as best she could.

Every now and then she tried to tell Him little bits of history that she thought He would understand—about how God had watched over His people in this very place and how He had brought them out of bondage into freedom in the happy, happy land where they were going now.

STORY 2

Happy Days in Nazareth

MILE after mile they journeyed back along the road on which they had fled from Herod. Somehow it didn't seem so far now, for they were going home, home, home!

At each stopping place Joseph asked other travelers for news, for there were no newspapers in those days. He had been away so long that he wanted to catch up on everything. What was the price of corn in Jerusalem? How much were carpenters earning nowadays? What had the Romans been doing of late?

One piece of news troubled him. Herod had been succeeded by his son Archelaus, who was reported to be as cruel as his father. Perhaps he, too, was looking for the baby who had escaped from Bethlehem.

Joseph and Mary had planned to go and live in the little town where their precious Jesus had been born; but now this was impossible. So they decided to go on to Nazareth, which they had left at the time of the taxing by Caesar Augustus.

Some days later they arrived at their old home town, and started life anew. Joseph opened up his carpenter's shop again and Mary began housekeeping. As for Jesus the Bible says that He "grew, and waxed strong in spirit, filled with wisdom: and the grace of God was upon him."

What a fine boy He must have been! So strong, so healthy, so good looking! With His perfect little body I am sure He could run faster and jump higher than any other boy or girl in town. With His marvelous eyesight and hearing He saw and heard everything that went on around Him. He missed nothing, and stored up all sorts of priceless memories for use in days to come.

So He grew not only in size like the other children of Nazareth, but in knowledge and wisdom too. In this His mother helped Him, of course. I am sure Mary took Him on many a walk into the hills and fields around Nazareth, pointing out all the beauties of nature and answering His many, many questions about them.

What a privilege Mary had, showing the flowers, the trees, and the animals to Him who, long, long ago created them! Perhaps this was why Jesus was so very interested in everything. Maybe deep down inside Him there was a strange feeling that somehow all these lovely things were really His and belonged to Him more than to anyone else in all the world.

Tenderly He would pick the lilies of the field and marvel at the beauty of their colors and the daintiness of their petals. Can't you hear Him saying to His mother, "Who made these beautiful things, Mamma?"

Watching a sparrow flit from tree to tree, or counting the speckled eggs in a thrush's nest, He would tell Mary of the wonder that filled His heart. "How do little birds come from eggs, Mamma?" He would ask, "And how do they know how to fly?"

I wish I could have been there to hear Mary's answers, don't you? But I am sure she always talked to Him with great patience, ever leading Him to honor and reverence His heavenly Father.

What wonderful bedtime stories Mary must have told Him before He went to sleep each night! I am sure she did her best to tell Him all she had ever heard or read about God's plan of salvation for the lost world. Beginning with the story of the Garden of Eden, and how Adam and Eve lost their lovely home because of Satan's trickery and their own sad mistake, she went on to tell how God planned to make everything right again.

"They didn't lose it forever, darling," I can hear her saying. "Oh, no. For God promised to send a little boy someday who would grow up to be big and strong and good and take it away from Satan and give it back to those who love and obey God."

And maybe Jesus said, with a faraway look, "I'd like to be that little boy, Mamma. I really would."

Then Mary would tell about Noah and the ark, the Flood and the rainbow—all those dear, sweet stories that mothers have told their children for thousands of years. And of course she told about Abraham, Isaac, and Jacob, and about Joseph and his brothers.

Then, too, there were the stories about Moses and how he led Israel out of Egypt through the Red Sea to Sinai, where God gave His people the Ten Commandments; about Joshua and the conquest of Canaan; about David and Solomon; about Daniel and Nehemiah.

Eagerly Jesus drank in every word. And when Mary would stop to say, "Now it's really time you went to sleep, dear," He would say, like any other little boy of His age, "Oh, just one more, please, Mamma! Just one more!"

I suppose there were some stories He liked better than others, such as the one about the three Hebrews in the fiery furnace, or about Abraham offering up Isaac on Mount Moriah, when he saw a ram caught in a thicket.

66

HAPPY DAYS IN NAZARETH

Now and then that strange look would come back on His eager face again, as He would say, "Sometimes, Mamma, I almost think I was there. I can see it all so clearly."

Day after day Mary would read the Holy Scriptures to Him, especially the chapters in the Old Testament where the prophets wrote about the coming of the Messiah. Jesus heard them so often that He soon knew them by heart and where to find them.

Every Friday evening the little family would kneel in prayer together to welcome the holy Sabbath. Next morning they would go to the synagogue for worship. It was a custom with them (Luke 4:16). They never missed. The preacher was always sure that Joseph, Mary, and that wonderful little boy of theirs would be in their places in the house of God.

How pleased the minister must have been to have a boy like that in front of him—so interested, so attentive, looking up with keen, wide-open eyes!

Thus it was that Jesus became "strong in spirit, filled with wisdom."

Knowledge of God's word made Him strong and wise, and as a result "the grace of God was upon him."

He was gracious at home and at play with other children. He was kind and unselfish, always trying His best to be help-ful. I am sure that Mary never had to ask Him twice to wash the dishes, and that there was never a word of grumbling when Joseph sent Him on an errand.

No doubt He was teased by other children because He took a stand for right and truth, but nothing they said or did could make Him say or do anything wrong. Others might cheat or lie, or tell shady stories, but not Jesus. And they always knew He would never go back on His word.

Don't you wish you could have known Him then? I do. And wouldn't it be wonderful if you could be as good and kind and truthful and courteous as He was? You can be if you will. This same Jesus, now Lord of glory, will help you if you ask Him. He understands all your problems so well, for, you see, once upon a time He was a boy too.

STORY 3

First Big Holiday

ONE by one the happy years of childhood slipped away. There came a day when Jesus had his fifth birthday. Then His sixth, His seventh, His eighth. And every passing year He became more and more the joy and wonder of His mother's heart.

Never had there been a little boy so good, so gentle, so friendly, so thoughtful of the needs of others; nor one so bright and intelligent.

By the time He was nine, ten, eleven, He must have been a wonderful help and comfort to His parents. He was always looking for ways to make life easier for them, mending this and fixing that and running quickly to do their bidding. And all the time His lovely voice filled the house with the melody of sacred songs.

At nighttime, after He had fallen asleep, I can see Mary sitting by His bedside marveling at the sweetness of His character as she thought of all the kind things He had said and done through another day.

Then she would think of Gabriel again, and what he had said to her: "He shall be great, and shall be called the Son of the Highest."

"No wonder He is so dear and good and beautiful!" I can hear her saying to herself. "Surely someone so full of love, so utterly unselfish, must be the Son of God."

All through these early years Jesus learned more and more about the Holy Scriptures. After Mary had taught Him how to read He began to study them Himself, and many were the questions He asked her about the meaning of texts that were not yet clear to Him.

Because of all that Mary had told Him from the time He was a baby, He was specially interested in all that the prophets said about the coming of a little boy who would grow up to

70

be the Deliverer of Israel and the Restorer of all that Adam and Eve had lost in Eden. Gradually He began to understand God's wonderful plan of salvation. Gradually, too, the truth dawned upon Him that He must be this child of destiny.

Exactly when this thought first came to Him we do not know, but when it did I am sure He became more serious as He tried to think His way through it all—what it would mean to Him, and the kind of life He would have to live.

When He became twelve years of age Mary and Joseph began talking to him about a trip to Jerusalem to celebrate the Passover.

There were three annual feasts that all the men of Israel were supposed to attend—Passover, Pentecost, and Tabernacles. The first was in the early spring, the second, seven weeks later, and the third was in the autumn, after the harvest. Everyone wasn't able to go to all of them, of course, but most people did their best to get to the Passover.

As Jesus was now a youth—twelve was the dividing line between childhood and youth in those days—Mary and Joseph felt that He should go with them this year; and you can imagine how happy Jesus was when He was told about it. Nineteen hundred years ago a trip to Jerusalem must have seemed very wonderful to a carpenter's son in Nazareth.

Can't you hear Jesus saying to Mary, "May I really go, Mother? Really? Do you mean it?"

Then they must have talked about all the things He would see in Jerusalem: the Temple, and Herod's palace, and all the old stores and houses. There would be priests offering sacrifices and Roman soldiers marching up and down the streets to keep order. And there would be all sorts of people, from far and near, crowding every nook and corner of the city.

The next few days were busy ones as Joseph tried to get his carpentry work done, Mary prepared food for the journey, and Jesus groomed the donkey and did what else He could to help get everything ready.

Then they were off.

To Jesus it was His first big holiday, and He enjoyed every minute of it.

When they reached the main road to Jerusalem they found it thronged with people, all going in the same direction. Jesus watched them with keenest interest, wondering, perhaps, whether they all understood why they were going there.

He understood, of course. Time and again He had talked

about the Passover with His mother. Now as He traveled toward the Holy City He could see that last night in Egypt, just before Moses led Israel out to safety, when God warned the people to sprinkle the blood of a lamb upon the lintel and doorposts of their homes, saying, "When I see the blood, I will pass over you."

To Jesus the Passover was something very sacred, bringing back memories of God's wonderful care for His people. But still there were questions in His mind. Why did God say a lamb should be killed? Why was the lamb's blood used in such a way? Could this be further proof that Messiah must suffer before He could save?

Surely someone in Jerusalem could tell Him. Maybe the priests, if they would listen to a boy. If He just got a chance, what a lot of questions He would ask them!

STORY 4

Teaching the Teachers

AS MARY, Joseph, and Jesus drew near to Jerusalem the highway became more crowded than ever. Jesus had never seen so many people in all His life. Thousands upon thousands were moving into the city from all directions for the Passover services.

As He caught sight of the city and saw the Temple standing on Mount Moriah He was greatly stirred. Old Bible stories that His mother had taught Him from childhood suddenly took on new meaning.

How wonderful to be looking at the very place where Abraham offered up Isaac, where David defeated the Jebusites, and Solomon reigned in all his glory! Here the prophets of God had spoken for a thousand years and more!

Yes, and someday Messiah would come to this city. He would ride upon a colt, "the foal of an ass," as Zechariah had prophesied.

Well may Jesus have said to Himself, "Someday, in God's

74

good time, I shall ride along this road and through these very gates!"

Inside the city at last, the holy family were soon very busy. They had to find a place to stay, buy food, then go on to the Temple, where the first Passover services were about to begin.

Jesus watched everything with wide-open eyes, for it was all so new to Him. He wondered why there were so many poor people, so many beggars, so many sick, and His loving heart went out to them all. He wanted to help them, and I expect Mary and Joseph had a hard time keeping Him from giving away every penny He had brought with Him.

When they arrived at the Temple Jesus was surprised to find that it looked more like a cattle market than a place of worship. Merchants were selling oxen, sheep, lambs, and birds to the people who had come to worship. Money-changers were noisily arguing with visitors about exchange rates.

75

"But why do they do it here?" I can hear Jesus saying to Mary. "It's not right, Mother! It's not right!"

"I know, dear," Mary may have said. "But they have done it so long that nobody thinks there's anything wrong about it."

"But the Scriptures say, 'My house shall be called the house of prayer'—not a shambles like this!"

To a boy brought up as Jesus had been it must have been a terrible shock to find such things going on in the holy Temple, but it was only the first of many disappointments He suffered.

He saw rich people drop gold and silver coins into the offering box with a loud noise, then look around to make sure their gift had been noticed; and He didn't like it. He saw poor people made to wait just because they were poor; and He didn't like that either. Worse still was the formal way in which the sacrifices were offered. Most of the people were doing it because it was a custom, and not because, deep down in their hearts, they were sorry for their sins.

As the days slipped by, Jesus longed more and more to talk to some of the priests and ask them about these things and all the other questions He had kept in His heart so long.

At last His chance came. There was a room in the Temple

buildings where young people were taught by rabbis during the big feasts. While his parents were busy elsewhere Jesus found His way here, and sitting down among other boys of His age, looked up at the bearded old teacher with rapt attention.

Never had He been so happy! This was what He had longed for! Pretty soon His hand shot up.

"May I ask a question?" said this lad with the bright eyes and the open, earnest face.

"Certainly, my boy," the teacher said. "What is it?"

Then came that first question, which showed such a knowledge of the subject that the teacher was shocked.

I wish I knew what that question was, don't you? Somehow I feel sure that it had to do with the prophecies about the Messiah. The teacher may have said that Messiah would come and reign as a king in glorious splendor; and Jesus may have asked, "But what about the prophecy in Isaiah, 'He was wounded for our transgressions, he was bruised for our iniquities'?"

As the rabbi answered, Jesus came back with another question and another, each one more pointed than the last.

TEACHING THE TEACHERS

Other rabbis drifted in to see what was going on, and stayed to listen to this remarkable child who knew the Holy Scriptures so well and seemed aware of hidden meanings these famous teachers had never thought about before.

After a while they began to ask Him questions.

"Where were you born?"

"In Bethlehem of Judea."

"Where do you live?"

"In Nazareth of Galilee."

"Where did you go to school?"

"I didn't go to school."

"Then how did you learn the Scriptures so well?"

"My mother taught Me."

Then they asked Him more questions to see how much He knew about the writings of patriarchs and prophets, and Jesus never missed one of them. So quick and right were His answers that they were all amazed. The Bible says that "all that heard him were astonished at his understanding and answers."

Hour after hour they talked together like this. Nobody got tired or hungry. The Passover services came to an end, and the thousands of visitors began to go home. But the priests and rabbis stayed on with this young lad from Nazareth who had stirred their hearts as no one else had done in many a long day.

As for Jesus, He was enjoying Himself so much that it never dawned on Him that His parents might already be on their way to Galilee. But they were. And soon they would be hunting for Him all over Jerusalem.

79

After the Passover services had come to an end Jesus slipped away from His parents and went to the Temple to reason with the rabbis. They marveled at His knowledge of the Scriptures.

STORY 5

Lost Boy Found

EXACTLY how far Joseph and Mary had gone on their way home when they missed Jesus we shall never know. The Bible says it was "a day's journey," and that could have been no more than a dozen miles or so, with the narrow roads crowded with people returning to their homes from the Passover.

All this time they had been chatting pleasantly with friends, talking about the happenings of the past few days in Jerusalem.

Most likely it was in the early evening, when they stopped to rest for the night, that they first noticed that Jesus wasn't with them. They had thought He was close behind them, but they hadn't bothered to make sure. Now, when they expected Him to come running to help them attend to the donkey and do other odd jobs, as He always did, no Jesus came.

"Jesus!" they called anxiously, as they looked the crowd over. "Where are you? We're waiting for you!"

80

LOST BOY FOUND

They felt sure He must be somewhere in that vast crowd, perhaps talking with other boys of His age. But He wasn't.

"Je-sus! Je-sus!" they called again and again, but their voices were lost amid the chatter of the people, the barking of dogs, the braying of donkeys, and the squeak and crunch of wagons going by.

After a while, when Jesus did not answer, Joseph and Mary began to get anxious. Now they started to look for Him in earnest.

"We've lost our son," they said to friends and strangers alike. "Have you seen Him anywhere?"

"Sorry, no," came the reply. "When did you last see Him?" they asked.

"Not since we were in Jerusalem. We thought He was right behind us."

"Too bad. Maybe you'd better go back."

Go back! All that way!

At first Joseph and Mary felt annoyed. Why hadn't He kept up with them? they asked. But then they remembered how Herod had sought to take His life. Could He still be in danger? Had some harm come to Him?

With fear gripping their hearts, they started back to Jerusalem. Anxiously they peered through the gathering darkness at everybody traveling in the opposite direction. But there was no sign of Him anywhere.

Passing through the city gates, they went back to the place where they had stayed. They hoped He might be there, waiting for them. But He wasn't.

They knocked on the doors of nearby houses.

"Excuse us, please, but we've lost our son. Have you seen Him? He's just twelve years old, and we brought Him here for the Passover."

"Sorry, no."

It was the same everywhere. Nobody had seen Him. Nobody knew anything about Him.

For hours and hours they searched.

"Where shall we try next?" I can hear Joseph saying.

"There's the Temple," Mary may well have said. "You know how He loved being there."

So to the Temple they went.

Exactly what time it was we

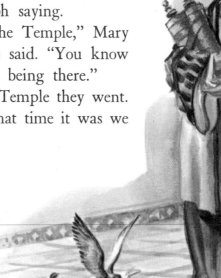

don't know. But the great Passover crowds were gone and the usual quietness had settled down again.

They saw a priest going by.

"Have you seen a boy about twelve years of age?" they asked him. "We can't find our son, and we wondered if He might be here."

"Do you mean the boy from Nazareth?"

"Yes! That's right. We are from Nazareth. Do you know where He is?"

"Well, He was over there in the young people's room. Several of the rabbis have been talking to Him. Maybe He's there still."

Quickly Joseph and Mary hurried across the courtyard. They found the room and stood outside listening. They could hear a man asking a question. One of the rabbis, no doubt. Then another voice answered, clear, soft, musical, but very steady and sure. There was no mistaking it. It was *His* voice! Thank God they had found Him at last!

Opening the door, they saw an unforgettable sight. There was their precious Jesus "sitting in the midst of the doctors, both hearing them, and asking them questions."

Mary was so glad to see Him that she forgot all about the learned doctors and ran over to Him with outstretched arms.

"Son," she said in tender rebuke, "why hast thou thus dealt with us? behold, thy father and I have sought thee sorrowing."

Just as lovingly Jesus answered, "How is it that ye sought

me? wist ye not that I must be about my Father's business?"

The meeting broke up, and the doctors began to leave. But some of them heard what Jesus said and wondered what He meant by "my Father's business." What business could He be doing for His father in the Temple? Hadn't He said His father was a carpenter? But Mary understood. As she looked into His eyes she knew that He had found something here while talking with these leaders of Israel. There was a new certainty in His voice. He was sure now that He must be the Messiah.

Mary knew, too, that when He spoke of His Father's business He was not thinking about Joseph, but God. Learning more about the Scriptures was God's business to Him. He was preparing Himself for the work He knew God had called Him to do.

Studying the Bible is still our Father's business—the most important business in the world. As we learn more of God's Word we shall gain wisdom for the work He wants us to do.

≋

STORY 6

The Carpenter's Son

≋

AS JOSEPH and Mary started off once more for Nazareth, this time with Jesus close beside them, they had much to talk about. Can't you hear Mary asking Jesus, "What did the doctors say to you, dear? And what did you say to them? Do tell us all about it."

What Jesus told them we do not know, but He surely had a tale to tell about the rabbis and all the questions they had asked Him and that He had asked them. Don't you wish you could have listened? I do.

No doubt as they journeyed on, Mary and Joseph told how they had come to miss Him that first night out of Jerusalem, and how they had sought for Him high and low till they went at last to the Temple.

I am sure they were very sorry that they had lost sight of their precious Son so long. They hadn't meant to; they had just been too wrapped up in other things and other people. How careful we must be not to let anything or anybody crowd

Him out of our thoughts! It is so easy to lose Him, so hard to find Him again.

A few days later they arrived in Nazareth, tired, but happy to be home again, safe and sound.

All that the Bible says about the next eighteen years of Jesus' life is found in this one text: "He went down with them, and came to Nazareth, and was subject unto them. . . . And Jesus increased in wisdom and stature, and in favour with God and man."

Eighteen years in twenty-eight words! Yet how much they tell!

He "was subject unto them." This means He was obedient and courteous to His parents, even in His teens, when some boys and girls cause so much trouble.

He did what He was asked to do cheerfully and graciously, never grumbling or complaining. His voice was often heard in song. He found His greatest joy in making His parents

86

happy, caring for their needs, and heeding their slightest wish.

What a wonderful example He set before us all! If you would be like Jesus you must be kind, loving, and obedient to *your* parents, helping them all you can.

As the years went by, He "increased in wisdom." This means that He did not stop studying at fifteen or sixteen, thinking He knew everything. He went on learning more and more—about the Bible, about nature, about people.

There were no high schools and universities then such as most young people of today can attend if they wish. Nor was there any public library in His town, where He could go and borrow books on any subject, as you can. Yet by reading all He could find in the synagogue, by exploring the secrets of nature, by mixing with all sorts of people, and above all, by talking with God in prayer, He became wiser than anyone who ever lived on earth either before or after Him.

He also "increased in . . . stature." This means that He was not a weakling. He paid attention to His health. He ate well and took lots of exercise. Knowing that He was to be the Messiah, He understood that He would need great strength to stand the strain. So He never let Himself begin bad habits of any kind. No doubt other boys in Nazareth did many foolish things that weakened their bodies and spoiled their characters —just as smoking and drinking spoil young people today— but Jesus would have nothing to do with them. His life was dedicated to a great purpose, as yours and mine should be.

Because of all this He "increased" also "in favour with God and man."

All heaven was watching this noble Youth. From the moment the angels had sung at His birth they had watched over Him everywhere He went. Just as they had rejoiced over the sweetest Baby ever born, so now they gloried in this grandest Youth who ever walked the earth.

And not only was heaven pleased with Him. For miles around Nazareth He was respected by men, women, and children alike. They loved Him because He was so gentle, kind, and friendly. They loved Him because He was so clean, pure, and truthful. They loved Him because He was so unselfish, so sympathetic, so thoughtful of others.

In the carpenter's shop He put His best into every job that Joseph gave Him to do. And what a pity it is that not one thing He made has been kept for us to see! A baby's crib, perhaps, a doll's bed, an armchair, or a chest of drawers. If such a thing existed, made by Jesus' own hands, it would be worth a fortune; but it would also be the finest example of faultless work for boys and girls today. How square would be the saw cuts! How exact the mitering! How smooth the surfaces! How invisible the joints! The finest cabinetmakers in the world would say, This is the work of a master craftsman!

PAINTING BY MANNING DE V. LEE

Sometimes, perhaps when He was eighteen, nineteen, or twenty—Jesus would wonder why He had to stay in a carpenter's shop so long. With the world waiting for the message He had to give, why waste time bending over a bench, planing wood, sharpening saws and chisels! Yet it was not time wasted. By striving always to do perfect work He was preparing Himself for the greater tasks ahead of Him.

In His heart He was sure He had come from heaven to earth to reveal God's love to men. And this meant showing love in all its beauty in the home, in the workshop, in the synagogue, along the city streets—anywhere, everywhere. It meant also setting an example of perfection in everything He did or said. He could never let Himself make one mistake, or let one poor, unworthy piece of work come from His hands, or let one unkind word fall from His lips.

What an example He set us! Today, nearly two thousand years later, He wants us to follow in His steps, to strive to live as He did. If we do, we too will "increase in wisdom and stature, and in favour with God and man."

PART III

Stories of Jesus' Ministry

(Matthew 3:1-4:22; Mark 1:1-20; Luke 3:1-4:13; John 1:1-4:42)

STORY 1

Exciting News

LIFE must have been very dull for the young people of Nazareth in those far-off days. They had no newspapers, radios, or television sets to tell them what was going on in the world about them. Apart from a few old books in the synagogue there was little or nothing for them to read.

Wages were small, and week by week they worked in the fields or shops to earn enough money to buy their food and pay their taxes. Apart from an occasional wedding or funeral nothing exciting ever happened.

Some believe that Joseph must have died about this time, for he is not mentioned again in the story of Jesus' life.

When Jesus had His twenty-first birthday He was still just a carpenter, working at His bench day after day, making furniture or maybe mending wagons or cart wheels for passing travelers.

Twenty-two, twenty-three, twenty-four. Slowly the peaceful, carefree years passed by. Spring, summer, autumn, winter,

93

Bidding His mother farewell Jesus went out from His quiet home at Nazareth to three and a half years of ministry, preaching to the poor, teaching the people, and healing the sick.

came and went, again and again. Harvest followed seedtime. Babies were born and old people died. But still nothing important disturbed the quiet of Nazareth.

Sabbath after Sabbath Jesus and His mother walked along the quiet streets to the synagogue and listened to some rabbi reading from the Holy Scriptures. It must have seemed to them that life in this old village might well go on like this for all time to come.

Then one day a man arrived with an unusual story, which quickly spread from one end of town to the other. Dropping into the carpenter shop he told Jesus about it. Down by the Jordan River, he said, at a place called Bethabara, a strange man had begun to preach. Hundreds of people were going out to listen to him, even from as far away as Jerusalem. So powerful was his message that the whole country was getting excited about it.

"What is his name?" Jesus no doubt asked.

"He calls himself John, and he says he is preparing the way for the coming of some great person who is to become the judge and ruler of Israel."

"Does he tell the people to rebel against the Romans?"

"Oh, no. Many Roman soldiers listen to him too. He just tells everybody to repent and stop doing wrong so that they will be ready to meet the Messiah when He comes among them."

"And then?"

"Well, then he baptizes them—puts them right under the water to show that their sins have all been washed away."

94

EXCITING NEWS

"Are many being baptized?"

"Oh, yes, hundreds and hundreds. It's a wonderful sight. You ought to go and see it."

This was indeed great news. And it must have been a solemn moment when Jesus told His mother about it.

I can hear Him saying, "Mother, Cousin John has begun to preach. I must go to him. The time has come."

Mary understood. She had feared something like this might happen someday. Now her mind went back to that far-off time —thirty years before—when Elisabeth told her what the angel Gabriel had said about her baby John. "He shall be great in the sight of the Lord," he had said. "And many of the children of Israel shall he turn to the Lord their God. And he shall go before him in the spirit and power of Elias, to turn the hearts of the fathers to the children, and the disobedient to the wisdom of the just; to make ready a people prepared for the Lord."

No doubt the time had arrived for Gabriel's words to come true. And if her own precious Jesus was indeed "the Son of the Highest," as Gabriel had said He was, He must be the one about whom John was now preaching.

Tenderly they said farewell, both knowing in their hearts that the happy days in Nazareth were gone for good.

Then, clearing His bench for the last time and carefully putting away the tools He would never use again, Jesus closed the door of His carpenter shop and set out for the Jordan.

It was the parting of the ways for Him. Behind Him lay the precious memories of boyhood and youth, with pleasant workdays and happy Sabbaths around His old home, and hours of bliss spent with His heavenly Father upon the mountain-side and in the nearby fields and forests.

Ahead were days of toil and sorrow, of temptation and trial. Messiah would be King someday, He knew, but He must die before He could reign. "A man of sorrows, and acquainted with grief" He would be. The Holy Scriptures said so. Yet He did not draw back. He must now begin the wonderful ministry of preaching, teaching, and healing to which God had called Him.

Striding bravely down the steep mountain trail, He made His way to John—to Bethabara, Gethsemane, and Calvary.

STORY 2

The Shining Light

THERE was no trouble finding John the Baptist. All roads to the Jordan were crowded with thousands of people going to listen to him.

As Jesus drew near and mingled with the throng He saw His cousin standing on a rock or a small knoll near the riverbank. He was a striking figure, clad not in the flowing robes of the rich and learned but in a garment made of camel's hair, with "a leather girdle around his waist." As he preached, his eyes seemed to flash fire, while his powerful voice boomed across the valley, imploring the people to turn from their sins and come back to God while yet there was time.

What a preacher! High and low, rich and poor, hung upon his words. No wonder Gabriel had said he would be like Elijah! He surely was. Just as Elijah had defied the prophets of Baal on Carmel, so John boldly rebuked the richest and most powerful men in Israel for their sins. Fearlessly he exposed the wickedness of Herod, even as Elijah had rebuked King

Ahab. He seemed to be, as Jesus said afterward, "a burning and a shining light."

Seeing some of the Pharisees and Sadducees in his congregation, he called them a "brood of vipers" and asked them, "Who warned you to flee from the wrath to come? Bear fruits that befit repentance."

Knowing what they were thinking, he added, "Do not begin to say to yourselves, 'We have Abraham as our Father'; for I tell you, God is able from these stones to raise up children to Abraham." Being children of Abraham wouldn't help them in the judgment if they weren't walking with God as did Abraham. Having the most famous man who ever lived as their father wouldn't help them a bit if they were not sorry for their sins.

"Even now the ax is laid to the root of the trees," he cried; "every tree therefore that does not bear good fruit is cut down and thrown into the fire."

This was a warning all could understand. Everybody in the crowd, at some time or other, had seen a barren tree cut down and burned. So they began asking themselves what sort of fruit their lives were bearing. Was it good or bad, sweet or sour, wholesome or rotten? They knew the answer. As the preacher's fiery words burned into their hearts it seemed as though God Himself were speaking to them. The "shining light" was breaking through every barrier, revealing all the darkness, the meanness, the cruelty, within.

"What shall we do?" they began to cry. And John replied, hitting hard at their selfishness, "He who has two coats, let him share with him who has none; and he who has food, let him do likewise."

There were tax collectors in the crowd, and they too cried out, "What shall we do?" Knowing their greed, John answered, "Exact no more than that which is appointed you." In other words, "Don't rob people by taking more taxes than you are supposed to."

Even some of the Roman soldiers, who had come to listen out of idle curiosity, were moved by John's fervent preaching. "What shall we do?" they asked. And John replied, "Do violence to no man, neither accuse any falsely; and be content with your wages."

Never had anyone had the courage to talk so plainly to the rich and the mighty as this remarkable man. And the amazing thing was that they took it from him and came back for more. Hundreds began to confess their sins and, forming a long line, moved down to the river to ask the prophet to baptize them. Pharisees, Sadducees, tax collectors, and soldiers mingled with the common people as John dipped them one by one in the waters of the Jordan. Nothing like this had ever been seen in Israel before. Surely a great new day was dawning!

"Thank God!" the people said one to another after the meeting, as they sat around sharing their lunches as John had bidden them. "At last another prophet has risen among us!"

"He must be Elijah, risen from the dead!" some said, while others whispered, "He could be the Messiah. He is just the man to deliver us from the Romans."

And Jesus, listening, wondered and waited.

STORY 3

A Voice From Heaven

THAT whispered word spread like wildfire.

"The Messiah!"

From group to group it swept till everybody in the crowd was looking at John with a great hope in his heart. Perhaps this mighty preacher, who could so move hearts that even Pharisees and Sadducees humbly asked for baptism, might be the very One for whom all Israel had been waiting so long.

Then somebody told John, and he was shocked.

"No, no!" he cried. "I am not the Christ. I am only His messenger, sent to prepare the way before Him."

"Are you Elijah, then?" someone asked.

"No, not Elijah," said John.

"Then who are you?"

"I am the voice of one crying in the wilderness, Make straight the way of the Lord."

"If you are not the Christ or Elijah," asked a Pharisee, "why are you baptizing people?"

100

A VOICE FROM HEAVEN

Said John, "I baptize with water: but there standeth one among you, whom ye know not; he it is, who coming after me is preferred before me, whose shoe latchet I am not worthy to unloose."

"What does he mean?" the people must have asked. "Is the Messiah already among us? Is He somewhere in this crowd?"

They began to look around. But they couldn't see anybody who looked like the Messiah they expected. Surely John must be mistaken. There was nobody here whose shoes he wasn't worthy to untie. It was all very strange. They wished John wouldn't be so mysterious sometimes.

While everybody was talking and wondering what John meant, a young Galilean about thirty years of age began moving closer to the riverbank. Nobody took any special notice of Him. He was just one of the crowd going to be baptized.

Suddenly John looked up. As he caught sight of Jesus a strange look came upon his face.

In all the hundreds of people who had come to him for baptism he had never seen anyone like this. Purity, goodness, nobility, shone from His clear eyes and kindly face. There was something strangely Godlike about Him. Surely this must be the Messiah!

As Jesus asked for baptism John refused.

"Oh, no," he said. "You should baptize me."

But Jesus insisted. "Let it be so," He said. He wanted to "fulfil all righteousness." He had no sins to be washed away, but wished to set a perfect example before all who should follow Him. Had He not been baptized, others would have had an excuse for saying that they need not be baptized either; and Jesus knew that would not be good for them.

John at last agreed. Gently he lowered Jesus into the Jordan until the water covered Him completely. Then, just as carefully, he lifted Him again to His feet.

At that very moment something marvelous happened. The Bible says that as Jesus went up out of the water, "lo, the heavens were opened unto him, and he saw the Spirit of God descending like a dove, and lighting upon him: and lo a voice from heaven, saying, This is my beloved Son, in whom I am well pleased."

How very, very wonderful! Amid all the jostling crowd His Father had recognized Him and called Him "my . . . Son"!

From all His mother had told Him, and from all His study of the Scriptures, He had believed He must be the Son of God, sent to be the Saviour of the world; now He was doubly sure, beyond all possibility of doubt.

All heaven had been waiting and watching for this moment: for now it was that the precious Babe of Bethlehem, the noble Youth of Nazareth, became "Messiah the Prince," the "anointed One"—anointed by the Holy Spirit of God. And it happened at the exact time foretold by Gabriel to Daniel long years before.

Now, after thirty years of preparation; of study, work, and worship; Jesus was ready to begin His ministry of love that had been planned for Him "from the foundation of the world."

How beautiful it was that on this very day His Father should say to Him, "This is my beloved Son, in whom I am well pleased." Just to know that His Father loved Him and was pleased with Him must have meant more to Jesus than we can ever imagine.

You like your father to be pleased with you, don't you? Of course you do. So Jesus was made happy, too, by His Father's words of praise. New courage filled His heart. Now He could go on to meet anything that might happen to Him in the days ahead.

STORY 4

The Lamb of God

SEEING the glorious light upon the head of Jesus, and hearing the voice from heaven, John knew for sure that he had just baptized the Messiah.

Now, pointing to Jesus, he said, "Behold the Lamb of God, which taketh away the sin of the world."

The people around must have wondered what he meant. How could any man be "a lamb"? How could this young Galilean, this carpenter of Nazareth, take away the sin of the world?

Even John himself may not have fully understood the words he had been led to speak. But Jesus did. His mind went back to the first time He had seen a lamb offered as a sacrifice in the Temple. He remembered, too, how lambs were killed in all the homes of Israel just before the great deliverance from Egypt.

It was all of a pattern, and the pieces were fitting together one by one. More and more clearly He saw that He too must

M. deV. Lee

be offered as a sacrifice before He could fulfill His purpose to
take away sin from the world forever.

Moments later John began to baptize again, and the long
line of men and women, boys and girls, was moving slowly
by as he lowered them one by one into the water.

Few, if any, gave another thought to what the Baptist
had said to Jesus, but because of what happened later on Calvary
those strange but wonderful words of his have lived on down

106

the ages. Today they are reckoned among the most beautiful words ever spoken. Every time we look at a picture of Jesus, or think of Him hanging upon the cross, we cannot but hear John saying again, "Behold the Lamb of God, which taketh away the sin of the world."

Jesus was indeed God's precious Lamb, His only-begotten Son. Only very great love—love beyond our understanding—could have led Him to give this Lamb to die for us. But that is just what He did.

When Abraham and Isaac were climbing Mount Moriah, you remember, the boy said to his father, "Behold the fire and the wood: but where is the lamb for a burnt offering?" Abraham replied, "My son, God will provide himself a lamb." A little while later he saw "a ram caught in a thicket" and the boy's life was saved.

Now once more God had provided a lamb, His own dear Son, that the lives of many boys and girls might be saved. This dear Lamb was not to die yet, for the time had not come. But someday—in just a little while—He would pay the price of sin for everybody.

This is what John meant when he said that Jesus would "take away the sin of the world."

Sin, which is another name for disobeying God, brings death. God made this plain to Adam and Eve before they ate the forbidden fruit in the Garden of Eden. But they took no notice of what He said and so had to pay the penalty.

There was no way out, no way back to Eden and to the life they had lost, unless someone should bear the penalty for them. And this is what Jesus came to do. Not only for Adam and Eve, but for you and me and everybody.

By coming to this world as the Lamb of God, and dying in our stead, He made it possible for us to live forever—just as Adam and Eve might have done if they had never done wrong.

But this is not the only way Jesus takes away the sin of the world. Boys and girls who truly love Him and believe that He is the Son of God soon find out that they do not want to do anything bad any more. Somehow the love of Jesus so fills their hearts that they want to be as good, and kind, and true, and honest, as He was.

So Jesus, the Lamb of God, not only took upon Himself the penalty of sin, but also broke the power of sin.

What a wonderful plan it was! And how beautifully simple! In a word, it was to love us out of sin! Someday, Jesus thought, if only He gave us all His love we would begin to love Him. Then we would long to be good, just to please Him. At last, there would come a time, in a wonderful earth made new, when everybody would love Him and want to be like Him. Then nowhere, in all the wide, wide world, would one little sin be found.

This was His hope and His dream; and you and I can help to make it come true by asking Him to take away sin from our hearts today.

108

STORY 5

Battle in the Wilderness

A FTER His baptism Jesus did not at once begin to teach and heal. Instead He disappeared and nobody knew where He had gone.

John kept on preaching, but Jesus went off by Himself, walking mile after mile into the wild, desolate country that borders the Jordan valley.

The Bible says, "And Jesus being full of the Holy Ghost returned from Jordan, and was led by the Spirit into the wilderness."

He wanted to be alone, away from the noisy crowds. He wanted to be able to think of all that had happened at His baptism. The memory of it was so very sacred He could not share His thoughts with anybody.

His Father had spoken to Him! He had called Him "my beloved Son." He had said He was well pleased with Him! What a glorious moment that had been!

Yes, and He could still feel the thrill that surged through

His whole being as the Spirit of God came upon Him. Now as He strode along He was "full of the Holy Spirit." His every thought was holy. He had but a single purpose—to do the will of His Father with all His heart and mind and soul.

Coming to some shady spot, perhaps under some overhanging rock, He rested, and lifting His eyes heavenward, talked with His Father.

What a beautiful prayer that must have been! What a pity nobody was there to write it down so that we might know what He said!

No doubt He gave thanks for the divine watchcare that had been over Him from His birth in Bethlehem till now; for the happy, peaceful days in Nazareth; and especially for His mother's love.

Then, as He thought of what it meant to be the Son of God, the Messiah of Israel, the Saviour of the world, how He must have prayed for wisdom and strength and courage to do all that His Father expected of Him!

BATTLE IN THE WILDERNESS

Most earnestly He prayed that the peace and love of Heaven might fill His soul and flow out to others in deeds of kindness and mercy. "Help Me, dear Father," He may well have cried, "to let everybody see that God is love."

Hour after hour He prayed, scarcely noticing the passing of time. The sun set and rose again upon Him while still He talked with His Father. Day after day of sweet communion slipped by.

Wild beasts found His hiding place, but they did not seek to hurt Him. A prairie dog came to sniff, a mountain lion peered round a giant boulder, an eagle flew low down the canyon and perched on a nearby crag, but it was only to look and wonder. They seemed surprised to find their good Creator here.

Jesus had brought no food with Him, and there was none to be found in the desert. So He did not eat. Yet so deep in thought was He that not till forty days and forty nights had passed did He feel hungry.

Then it was that He became aware that He was not alone in the wilderness. Somebody had followed Him. Somebody evil. Somebody who hated Him.

The Bible tells us that after nearly six weeks of fasting, when His body must have been very weak indeed, Satan began to tempt Him.

Then followed the great battle in the wilderness between the Prince of light and the prince of darkness.

They had met before in heaven when Satan was known as Lucifer, and Christ had cast him out because of his wickedness.

111

They had met in the Garden of Eden after Satan had spoiled God's beautiful plan for this world by deceiving Adam and Eve.

Now they met again in this lonely desert place, with Satan eager to destroy the Saviour before His ministry could begin.

No doubt Gabriel was not far away, and legions of good angels stood ready to leap to Jesus' side if Satan should try to hurt Him at this time. But they stood aside and let the evil one speak to Him and deceive Him if he could.

How anxiously they must have watched this battle of minds and hearts, this contest of wits and words! How they wanted Jesus to win!

Well they knew how subtle Satan could be. Had he not deceived millions in the past four thousand years? How then could Jesus—so young, so weak, so hungry—stand against his wiles? How much of the wisdom of God had He stored up in His heart since His boyhood? Was it enough for this hour of temptation?

Thank God, it was.

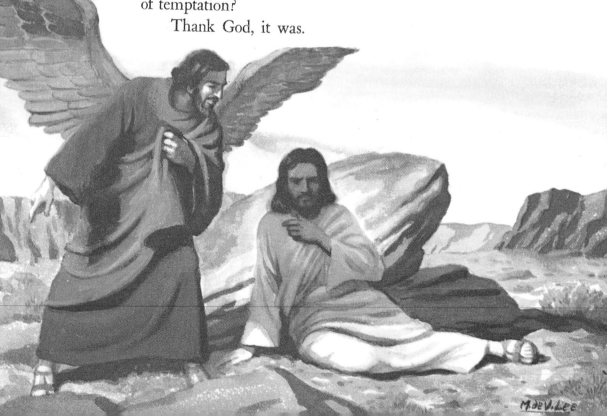

STORY 6

Three Terrible Temptations

HAVE you ever gone without food for one whole day? If so, how hungry did you feel? You don't need to tell me. I can guess.

Imagine having nothing to eat for *two* days, or even *three* days. Wouldn't that be awful! And if you had to go for a whole week without food I am sure you would be ready to eat the hardest crusts you could find anywhere.

Think then how Jesus must have felt after almost six weeks without food! How He lived all that time without any breakfast or lunch or supper I do not know. But He did. And then it was, when He was weakest, that Satan struck his first blow.

"If thou be the Son of God," he whispered in a kindly voice, "command that these stones be made bread."

It sounded so innocent, as temptations so often do. Satan spoke as if he were just trying to be helpful. The ground where they stood was covered with stones, and if Jesus was really the Son of God, it would be perfectly easy for Him to make just one or two of them into bread. Nobody would know about it, and He would feel much better.

But Jesus saw through the devil's subtle plot. He scented danger in that little "if." Should He try to work such a miracle it would mean that He had a doubt in His mind about His relation to God. And how could He doubt when God had openly claimed Him as His own Son?

Jesus also saw that if He were to use His power to benefit Himself it would be a selfish act, and such a thing He could not and would not do.

He saw, too, that if He were to do this once, He would do it again and again until the whole purpose for which He had come into the world would be spoiled. People would come to Him not to learn about God but to get free food and clothes and houses and money. It would be very easy for Him to gather a great following this way, but it would not be God's way.

So, terribly hungry though He was, He refused, saying to Satan, "It is written, Man shall not live by bread alone, but by every word that proceedeth out of the mouth of God."

Now Satan led Him to Jerusalem, and they stood together on the highest part of the Temple. Looking down, Jesus saw that it was a long way to the ground. One false step and He would plunge onto the rocks below. Satan could easily have tried to push Him over, but he didn't. He had something worse in mind.

Quoting Scripture himself this time, to make this second

temptation seem more innocent than the first, he said, "If thou be the Son of God, cast thyself down: for it is written, He shall give his angels charge concerning thee: and in their hands they shall bear thee up, lest at any time thou dash thy foot against a stone."

How very proper it sounded! Jesus was to claim a Bible promise and act upon it. Why not?

But there was that nasty "if" again, and Jesus did not like it. Of course He believed the promise, but He was not going to claim it for Himself just to put on a show for Satan's benefit. The power of God was not to be used for such a purpose or for the taking of an unnecessary risk. So He said to Satan, "Thou shalt not tempt the Lord thy God."

With His clear mind Jesus saw an even deadlier peril in this temptation. Like the first, its chief purpose was to ruin His mission to the world. He saw that if He jumped, and was miraculously saved from death, people would flock to Him as to a magician. They would point to Him as "the man who jumped from the Temple." He wanted no such cheap advertisement. He had come to save people by love, not by acrobatics and circus stunts. The devil's suggestion was opposed to every principle for which He stood. He refused to listen to it.

Defeated again, the devil tried a new approach. He led Jesus to a mountaintop. Here, looking north, south, east, and west, they could see many a city and village below them. Satan went on to talk of the glories of Memphis and Damascus; of Athens, Corinth, and Rome. Indeed, he showed Jesus "all the kingdoms of the world, and the glory of them," and said to Him, "All these things will I give thee, if thou wilt fall down and worship me."

The devil knew all about Jesus' plan to set up a kingdom and that He expected to do it the hard way, by sacrifice and suffering, persuasion and love. So he offered Him a kingdom the easy way.

"You can have your kingdom now," he said, "and it won't cost you anything. Just kneel down and worship me and it's all yours."

It was indeed the easy way, but Jesus was not interested in setting up a kingdom like those of the world, full of vice and wickedness. His plan was far different. He sought a king-

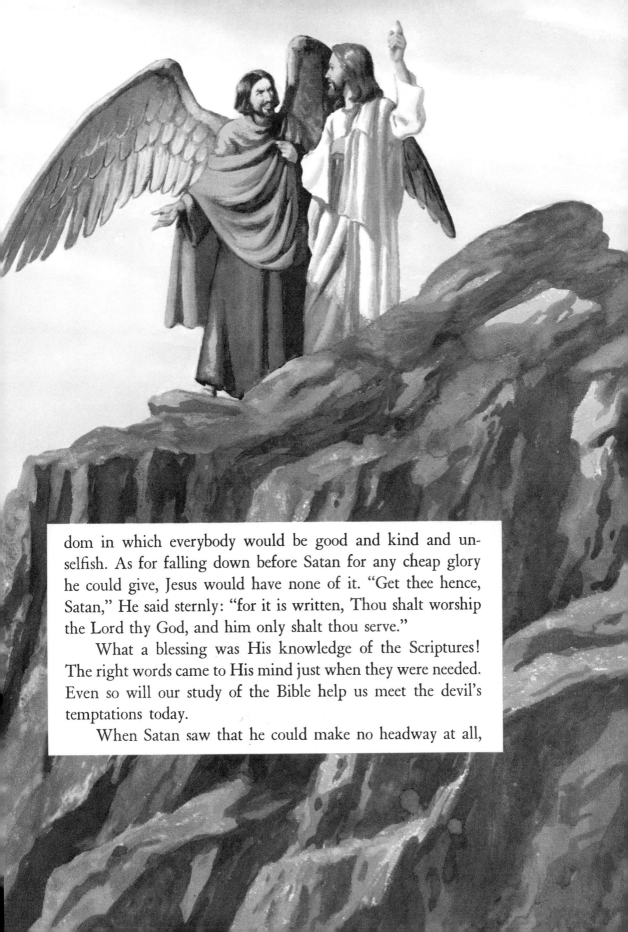

dom in which everybody would be good and kind and un-selfish. As for falling down before Satan for any cheap glory he could give, Jesus would have none of it. "Get thee hence, Satan," He said sternly: "for it is written, Thou shalt worship the Lord thy God, and him only shalt thou serve."

What a blessing was His knowledge of the Scriptures! The right words came to His mind just when they were needed. Even so will our study of the Bible help us meet the devil's temptations today.

When Satan saw that he could make no headway at all,

and that Jesus could not be moved one little bit from His loyalty to God, he went away. So will he leave us when he sees that we are determined at all costs to be true to God.

Then, the Bible says, "angels came and ministered unto him." Anxiously they had watched every moment of this awful struggle. Would Jesus be able to stand against "the wiles of the devil"? they had wondered. Would He win this dread battle with the prince of darkness?

Now that Jesus' victory was no longer in doubt, they pressed close to Him with gladness and, in ways unknown to us, brought Him food and comfort.

How long He tarried there we do not know, but as His strength began to return He set out for home.

Now there was a new light in His eye, a new confidence in His step and in His bearing. He had won the fight with His greatest enemy. He had proved that the worst temptations can be met and conquered. Tested, tried, and triumphant, He returned to the Jordan, back to the cities and villages of Israel, to begin the great work He had come into the world to do.

STORY 7

First Disciples

NOBODY can be sure, of course, but I like to think that Jesus came singing out of the wilderness. No doubt He was still pale from His weeks of fasting, but the Bible says that He "returned in the power of the Spirit."

He had just won a great victory over Satan. Angels had talked with Him and brought Him food. Forty days and nights alone with God had made heaven very near and real to Him and filled His heart with courage for the future.

Now, as He wended His way along the mountain trail, well may He have sung aloud that old familiar psalm His mother had taught Him long ago, "O give thanks unto the Lord, for he is good: for his mercy endureth for ever."

He had work to do, and He wanted to get at it. The hour had come for His message to be given to the world, and there was no time to lose. Now, as never before, He must be about His Father's business.

Who was the first to see Him and hear His voice as He

came down at last onto the plain of Jordan? Nobody knows. It could have been a shepherd minding his sheep or a farmer's wife milking a cow. And of course it *could* have been a group of boys and girls playing in a field. Looking up, they may have wondered who this friendly Stranger could be who smiled at them, waved His hand, and said, "The kingdom of God is at hand."

Coming to the river He may have found a weary traveler watering his donkey. To him, as to everybody else He met, He broke the good news about His coming kingdom.

"The time is fulfilled," said Jesus, "and the kingdom of God is at hand: repent ye, and believe the gospel."

"That's just how John the Baptist talks," the man may have said.

"Have you heard him preach?"

"Oh, yes. He's a great preacher. People are still crowding to hear him."

Jesus was anxious to see John again and to find out how he was getting on.

Mingling with the multitude, He came nearer to where His cousin was standing. Suddenly, as John caught sight of Him, he stopped speaking, and pointing right at Jesus, said, as he had once before, "Behold the Lamb of God, which taketh away the sin of the world."

Then he added, "This is he of whom I said, 'After me comes a man who ranks before me, for he was before me.' . . . I saw the Spirit descend as a dove from heaven, and it remained on him. I myself did not know him; but he who sent me to baptize with water said to me, 'He on whom you see the Spirit descend and remain, this is he who baptizes with the Holy Spirit.' And I have seen and have borne witness that this is the Son of God" (John 1:29-34, R.S.V.).

At once there was a mighty stir in the crowd. For weeks John had been saying that the Messiah was on His way, coming very soon. Now he was pointing at a man right in the congregation and saying, "This is He; this is the Son of God!"

People surged forward to catch a glimpse of the man John had pointed out. They pushed and shoved and trod on one another's toes. There was danger of a riot, and Jesus, not wishing to be a cause of trouble or the center of a mob scene, quietly withdrew. Unable to find Him, the people gradually settled down again to listen to John.

Two days later Jesus came to hear John again. As He walked among the people the Baptist caught sight of Him and called out once more, "Behold the Lamb of God!"

This time two men who heard these strange words followed Jesus out of the crowd. One of them was Andrew, the other, John—the John who, years later, wrote the Gospel that bears his name. Both were fishermen from Bethsaida, on the Sea of Galilee.

Noticing that He was being followed, Jesus turned and spoke to the two young men.

"What do you seek?" He asked.

"Rabbi," they said to Him, "where do you live?"

"Come and see," He said, leading the way to His humble dwelling.

Because it was nearly sunset Jesus invited them both to stay with Him, and they did. That brief visit changed not only their lives but the lives of millions of others. Actually it was the first meeting of the Christian church!

What Jesus said to Andrew and John during those few precious hours they were together we do not know. No doubt they asked Him what the Baptist meant by calling Him "the Lamb of God," and Jesus told them all about Himself and the kingdom of love He had come to set up.

Maybe they didn't understand all He said, but there was something about His voice and His manner that made them feel sure that it all must be true. As for His eyes, they seemed to look right through them, as though Jesus knew everything about them, all they had ever done or were going to do.

123

In that one short evening He won them both. They were His first disciples.

Next morning Andrew, in great excitement, hurried off to find his brother Simon.

"We have found the Messiah, the Christ," he said. "Come and meet Him."

Simon, another fisherman, wondered what this was all about. Should he go, or shouldn't he? But Andrew persuaded him and "brought him to Jesus."

Jesus gave him a smile of welcome and said, to the fisherman's amazement, "Your name is Simon but from now on it will be Peter." And so it was. Everybody has called him Peter from that day to this.

They were by Galilee now, and the little fishing boats were bobbing about on the blue water.

"Follow me," said Jesus, "and I will make you fishers of men. And they straightway left their nets, and followed him."

124

FIRST DISCIPLES

Soon others joined the little group. Jesus found Philip, and Philip found Nathanael, saying to him, "We have found him, of whom Moses in the law, and the prophets, did write, Jesus of Nazareth, the son of Joseph."

"Oh, no," said Nathanael, "I can't believe that. Can any good thing come out of Nazareth?"

"Come and see," said Philip, and Nathanael followed him.

Then a strange thing happened. When Jesus saw Nathanael coming toward Him, He said, "Behold an Israelite indeed, in whom is no guile!"

"How do you know me?" asked Nathanael, astonished.

"Before Philip called you," said Jesus, "when you were under the fig tree, I saw you."

Nathanael was overcome. How could Jesus have seen him under the fig tree? It was impossible. And yet, perhaps——

"Rabbi," he cried, as light dawned upon his mind, "thou art the Son of God; thou art the King of Israel."

STORY 8

Jesus Begins to Preach

SETTING out with His little group of disciples, Jesus went from village to village in Galilee, telling over and over again the good tidings of His kingdom.

Everywhere He went He found that John had indeed prepared the way before Him. Almost everybody was interested in what He had to say. They wanted to know more. They loved the simple, gentle, confident way He talked about the things of God. And they were thrilled by His knowledge of the Holy Scriptures. Whenever He quoted passages from the books of the prophets they seemed alive with new meaning.

At first He was invited to speak in the synagogues, and the people crowded in to hear Him. Never had they listened to such wonderful preaching. The Bible says that "they wondered at the gracious words which proceeded out of his mouth."

Some people, of course, didn't like Him. They said He was just another rabble rouser trying to stir up the Jews against the Romans. But nobody could listen to Him for long without

126 ·

knowing this wasn't true, for His was a mission of peace.

Jesus made it as plain as He could that His kingdom was quite different from any other kingdom anybody had ever heard of. It was a kingdom of love, and anyone could belong to it any time he wished. No war, no fighting, was needed to set up this kingdom, and the price of admission was a wish and a prayer—a wish to be good and a prayer of repentance.

As for the Romans, there was no need to worry about them. Just love them, said Jesus, and all would be well. If they should order you to carry a load one mile, carry it two miles. If they should take away your coat, offer them your shirt too. The toughest tyrant would soon soften if treated like that.

Someday, said Jesus, all the kingdoms of the world would pass away and God's kingdom of love would fill the earth. Paradise would be restored. Those who had let the love of God flood their hearts would find their way to the long-lost Garden of Eden. In that day there would be no more hatred or strife.

Everybody would love everybody else. Kindness, gentleness, sympathy, would have driven out everything hateful and ugly.

Such teaching was so new and beautiful that the people drank it up. Little synagogues, which had been half empty for years, suddenly became filled to overflowing with eager listeners.

Soon word spread everywhere that another great preacher had arisen, more wonderful even than John. Groups gathered around Him on the streets, asking questions and marveling at the wisdom of His answers.

They were amazed that He knew so much, in spite of the fact that He had never been to college, not even to one of the schools of the rabbis. But, best of all, they loved the way He took a personal interest in everybody. No matter who talked to Him—man, woman, or child—He had the same kindly smile and gracious word for all. He knew just what to say to make everyone feel better. After being near Him just a little while the people went away with a glow in their hearts.

No wonder the Bible says, "They were astonished at his doctrine: for his word was with power."

≈≈≈≈≈≈≈

STORY 9

Wedding Surprise

≈≈≈≈≈≈≈≈≈≈≈

BY THIS time Jesus had been away from home many weeks. Now as He drew near to Nazareth again I am sure He looked forward eagerly to seeing the familiar old place once more and greeting His mother at the gate.

But it was not to be, just now.

As He and His little band of followers climbed the steep, winding road from the lake, they came to the village of Cana, just six miles or so east of Nazareth, where they had been invited to a wedding. People in their best clothes were going into one of the houses. Oxcarts were parked outside and donkeys were tethered here and there.

"Looks as though everyone is here already," I can hear Peter saying. "What a lot of guests! Wonder if there are any here we know."

Then it was that Jesus caught sight of Mary, for she was at the wedding.

"Mother!" He cried, greeting her with gladness.

How happy they must have been to meet again, though Mary noticed at once how He had changed. He looked older and thinner, yet still He was her own dear Son.

"Meet my friends," I am sure Jesus said, introducing Andrew, Peter, John, Philip, and Nathanael.

"Come in! and welcome!" said Mary.

So Jesus and His friends sat down among the other guests, to some of whom, no doubt, they were strangers.

"That's Mary's Son," whispered one, nodding in the direction of Jesus. "I hear He's become quite a preacher."

"Yes," said another. "Some say He preaches even better than John the Baptist."

"Maybe He will speak in our synagogue some day. We must get the rabbi to ask Him."

"Is it true John the Baptist said He is the Messiah?"

"I heard so; but I never thought the Messiah would look like that. Isn't the Messiah coming as a king?"

So the guests may have talked as they ate the good things provided for them at the feast.

Meanwhile Jesus, ever friendly, chatted with those around Him, letting them see that He was glad to share their happiness.

By-and-by Mary came over to where Jesus was sitting, and whispered, "They have no wine."

She looked worried, and no wonder! This was serious— just as though your mother found that the punch was gone halfway through your birthday party.

For years Mary had counted on Jesus to help her out of difficulties and He had never failed her. Now,

130

motherlike, she turned to Him again. And so sure was she that He would know what to do that she said to the servants, "Whatever He says to you, do it."

Pointing to six large stone jars standing near the door, Jesus said, "Fill the waterpots with water."

The servants looked at the six jars and back again to Jesus. "What can He mean?" they wondered. "Doesn't He understand that it's wine that's wanted, not water?"

But Mary had told them to obey, so they did.

After they had gone to the well and filled the six big jars to the brim, Jesus told them to pour some out and carry it to the man in charge of the feast. This must have seemed a very strange thing for Him to say.

The servants must have wondered whether they should do it or not. What would the master of ceremonies think if they turned up with a jug of water!

But again they obeyed, and something wonderful happened.

As they tipped up one of the waterpots they noticed that the water had changed color.

"Look!" they cried. "It isn't water! It's wine!"

They tasted it to make sure it was all right, and their eyes opened wide! What wine this was!

Amazed and happy, they carried it to the man in charge and poured some into his cup. He tasted it, and *his* face lighted up. Never had he tasted such wine as this.

Calling the bridegroom, he asked him why he had kept the best wine till the last. But the bridegroom, astonished, wondered what the man was talking about. He hadn't kept any wine at all. He had thought it was all gone. Where had this wine come from? Who had brought it? Wine like this wasn't to be found anywhere in Galilee.

Soon all the guests were holding up their cups for some of this delicious wine and asking the same questions about it.

But nobody could answer them. That is, not until the servants began to talk.

Then the guests crowded around the six stone waterpots.

"You really filled these with water?" they asked.

"Yes. At the well."

"And you put nothing else in them?"

"Nothing."

132

"And when you poured out the water it had turned to wine?"

"That's the way it was. We saw it with our own eyes."

"A miracle!" cried everybody. "A miracle!"

And so it was.

The Bible says, "This beginning of miracles did Jesus in Cana of Galilee, and manifested forth his glory; and his disciples believed in him."

Yet it was no miracle to Jesus. It was no more difficult for Him to turn water into wine in a waterpot than to do it in a grapevine. He was just beginning to reveal His power as the Son of God.

133

STORY 10

The Temple Cleansed

RIGHT after the wedding at Cana, for some reason that we do not know, Jesus went to Capernaum with "his mother and his brothers and his disciples." This meant a journey of seventeen miles or so down the steep mountain road to the lake.

But Jesus did not stay there long. After only "a few days" He started off for Jerusalem.

It was Passover time again—the first since His Father had openly declared Him to be the Son of God—and He felt He should spend it in the Holy City. This year, of all years, He must go there and let the great crowds know that the Messiah was among them.

How many of His disciples traveled with Him on this trip we do not know. A few at least went along, and precious must have been the hours they spent together with their Master.

As the unhurried hours slipped by He may have explained to them the true meaning of the Passover service, and why it

134

was that so many lambs had to be slain on that far-off night in Egypt before Israel escaped to the Promised Land. And He may have told them how the Lamb of God must some-day be slain that Israel may be delivered from the power of sin. Then all who sprinkle the blood of God's Lamb upon the doorposts of their heart will be saved in His kingdom.

On that long walk to Jerusalem they mingled with hundreds of other pilgrims who were going the same way. Many were weary and troubled, but somehow all felt better as Jesus passed by. Always He seemed to know the right words to say to cheer people up.

News of the miracle in Cana of Galilee had already spread far and wide, and every now and then someone would point to Jesus as the man who had turned water into wine. But soon people were talking about other miracles of His, for every time He touched the sick they became well again.

By the time Jesus and His little party reached Jerusalem many more people had come to love Him for His gracious words and kindly deeds. The Bible says that "when he was in Jerusalem at the passover . . . many believed in his name, when they saw the miracles which he did."

As He drew near to the Temple, His face, which had had such a gentle look as He had mingled with the common people, became stern. His keen ears had caught the noise of the market in the outer court. Plainly to be heard were the lowing of cattle, the bleating of sheep, the shouts of excited merchants, and the loud arguments at the tables of the money-changers. What a bedlam it was!

As a boy of twelve Jesus had heard this same noise and had wished He might do something about driving these worldly people out of this holy place, but it was too soon then. Now the time had come for Him to bear witness both to the truth and to the holiness of God. Had He not come into the world for this purpose? And what better time to begin than now?

Gathering up a few strands of cords that were lying around, Jesus twisted them together in the form of a whip. Then, lifting this in His right hand, He advanced in the power of the Spirit upon the merchants and money-changers.

"Take these things hence," He cried; "make not my Father's house an house of merchandise."

At first no one took any notice of Him. There was so much clamor, so much confusion.

So Jesus strode toward one of the money-changers and tipped up his table, scattering the money all over the place.

Furious, the man leaped to his feet, ready to tear the person apart who had dared to do this thing. But as he looked at Jesus and saw the glory of God upon His face, he fled in terror before Him.

Now another table was overturned, and another, and another, as Jesus, utterly fearless, drove everybody before Him. Frightened cattle began to run too.

"Get out! Get out!" He cried. "Take these things away! God said His house should be called a house of prayer, but you have made it a den of thieves!"

What a scene that was! Not one of those hardened merchants dared to defy Him. With their sheep and oxen they stampeded toward the Temple gates to get away from this Man with the blazing eyes.

At last all had gone and Jesus was left alone with His followers. Shekels by the thousands lay all over the place with nobody to pick them up.

It was a strange and startling beginning to Jesus' ministry in the capital of Israel, but He could not have chosen a better way to let the whole country know that the Messiah had arrived.

A few minutes after the last table had been overturned and the last shekel had stopped rolling across the pavement, all Jerusalem was talking about what had happened in the Temple. How the people loved it! All their lives they had hoped that someday somebody would have the courage to do just this! Now Somebody *had* done it, and those mean, cheating merchants and money-changers had fled before Him. It was too good to be true!

Of course, everybody began to ask who it was that had done so brave a deed and cleansed the Temple of this crowd of thieves.

Some said that it was a Galilean, a carpenter from Nazareth; others that it was the man who turned water into wine at Cana; while some said it was the very same person whom John the Baptist had called "the Lamb of God, which taketh away the sin of the world."

Then hope began to rise in many hearts as people asked one another, "Could this be the Messiah, the Saviour of Israel?"

≈≈≈≈≈≈≈≈≈≈

STORY 11

Midnight Visitor

≈≈≈≈≈≈≈≈≈≈≈≈≈≈

AFTER Jesus left the Temple court on that never-to-be-forgotten afternoon the merchants and the money-changers no doubt came right back, picked up their money, and started all over again.

But they were angry, as you can imagine. Their pride had been hurt. Everybody was laughing at them for running away from the gentle Carpenter of Nazareth. They vowed to get even with Him someday.

The priests were upset too. They didn't like the way this young reformer from the country had done what they should have done long ago.

But there were some among the leading people of Jerusalem who believed Jesus might be right. They had listened as He talked to the people, and they liked what He said to them. One of them, whose name was Nicodemus, decided to have a private talk with Jesus to find out more about Him.

But where was Jesus? Nobody seemed to know. Then

139

someone said He often went to the Mount of Olives in the
evening to rest and pray. Nicodemus decided to follow Him
there.

Waiting till darkness had fallen, so that none of his friends
would see where he was going, this famous ruler wrapped his
cloak about him and set out into the night.

How he found Jesus we do not know, but he did, and there
in the moonlight, looking down upon the sleeping city, they
talked about the kingdom of God.

"Rabbi," said Nicodemus, "we know that thou art a teacher
come from God: for no man can do these miracles that thou
doest, except God be with him."

Jesus was pleased to hear these gracious words from such
an important man, and O how He wanted to help him understand the truth about His kingdom of love!

"Except a man be born again," He said, "he cannot see
the kingdom of God."

Nicodemus looked puzzled.

"How can a man be born when he is old?" he asked.

140

Jesus must have smiled at this, for, of course, He was not talking about the birth of a baby, but about what happens in the heart when the Holy Spirit comes into it. The change is so complete it's like being born again.

Jesus tried to explain. Pointing to the trees that were swaying gently in the cool night breeze, He said, in other words, "You know the wind is blowing because you can hear the rustling of the leaves, but you can't tell where the wind comes from or where it goes. So it is with those who are born of the Spirit."

He wanted Nicodemus to know that the Holy Spirit comes into any heart that is open to Him. Nobody can understand exactly how it happens, but everybody can see the results. A boy or girl into whose heart the Holy Spirit has come is kind and true and gentle, loving good and hating evil.

This was all new to Nicodemus. Famous though he was for his wisdom, he still didn't understand this very simple truth.

"How can this be?" he asked.

"Are you a teacher of Israel," said Jesus, "and yet you don't understand this?"

Then Jesus went on to tell more about how hearts and lives can be changed by the power of God.

First, He reminded Nicodemus of the time when Moses put a brass serpent on a pole and everybody who looked at it was cured of snake bite. Then he said, "As Moses lifted up the serpent in the wilderness, even so must the Son of man be lifted up: that whosoever believeth in him should not perish, but have everlasting life."

Just one look at the Son of man will heal anyone of the bite of the great serpent Satan, and make him whole again.

Nicodemus did not answer. He was too taken aback by these strangely moving words. Who was this "Son of man"? he wondered. Could it be the Carpenter Himself?

Then Jesus spoke again, bringing to this earnest seeker after truth the most beautiful message that ever fell on human ears:

"God so loved the world, that he gave his only begotten Son, that whosoever believeth in him should not perish, but have everlasting life.

RUSSELL HARLAN, ARTIST

"For God sent not his Son into the world to condemn the world; but that the world through him might be saved."

Though spoken to but one man upon a dark and silent hillside long ago, these precious words have spread around the world as though broadcast from some powerful radio station. Millions upon millions have heard them and been moved to tears by them. They have come down across the ages in all their beauty and power.

And why? Because they are the very heart of the gospel—that message of love that Jesus came from heaven to bring to the world. They tell how anybody, anywhere—boy or girl, man or woman—may enter the kingdom of God and live happily forever and ever.

And what is the secret? Just this: Believe Jesus loves you. That's all. Nothing else. Nothing to buy. Nothing to pay. Nothing to do but this.

How simple! How beautifully, wonderfully simple!

Do you believe Jesus loves you? Really? Truly?

Then the kingdom is yours, now and always.

STORY 12

Sudden Harvest

AFTER the Passover, Jesus stayed awhile in Judea, teaching and healing the people. Then, with His disciples, He turned northward again toward Galilee.

On the way they stopped at a city called Sychar, which belonged to the Samaritans. These people, you remember, were descended from the strangers whom the King of Assyria brought into Palestine when he took the Israelites into captivity. Having lived here for hundreds of years, they felt that the country belonged to them just as much as to the Jews. But the Jews hated them and would have nothing to do with them.

While His disciples went into Sychar to buy food, Jesus, weary with the day's journey, sat down by a well. It was called Jacob's well because people believed Jacob had dug it when he passed this way.

Just then a Samaritan woman carrying a waterpot drew near. Setting down her pot, she lowered a bucket into the water

and hauled it up again. And as she did so Jesus spoke to her.

"Give Me a drink," He said.

The woman looked at Him in astonishment.

"How is it that you, a Jew, ask a Samaritan for a drink? The Jews have no dealings with the Samaritans."

But there were no national barriers in His heart. He loved everybody, no matter where he was born.

"If you had known who asked *you* for a drink," He said, "you would have asked *Him* for a drink and He would have given you living water."

"You don't have a bucket and the well is deep," said the woman. "Where do you keep this living water? Are you greater than our father Jacob who gave us this well?"

Jesus answered, in words that will live forever, "Whosoever drinketh of this water shall thirst again: but whosoever drinketh of the water that I shall give him shall never thirst; but the water that I shall give him shall be in him a well of water springing up into everlasting life."

The woman caught the meaning of the beautiful words, especially that "whosoever." She saw that it included even her, a Samaritan.

"Sir, give me this water!" she cried. "Then I shall never be thirsty again and never have to come here to draw water any more."

Jesus smiled at her eagerness, but He had a lesson to teach her.

"Go, call your husband and come back," He said.

The woman hung her head and said, "I have no husband."

147

← PAINTING BY KREIGH COLLINS   © 1956, BY REVIEW AND HERALD

When the woman at Jacob's well realized that Jesus loved everybody, even the Samaritans, she eagerly requested that He give her to drink of the living water He had promised her.

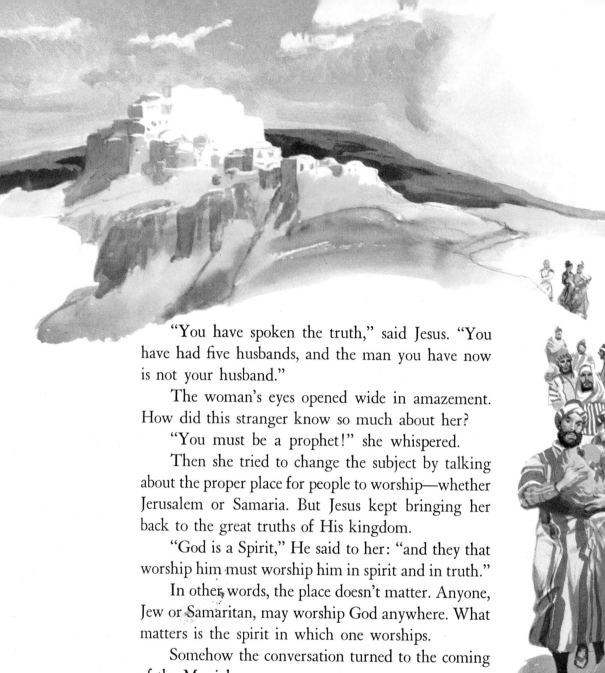

"You have spoken the truth," said Jesus. "You have had five husbands, and the man you have now is not your husband."

The woman's eyes opened wide in amazement. How did this stranger know so much about her?

"You must be a prophet!" she whispered.

Then she tried to change the subject by talking about the proper place for people to worship—whether Jerusalem or Samaria. But Jesus kept bringing her back to the great truths of His kingdom.

"God is a Spirit," He said to her: "and they that worship him must worship him in spirit and in truth."

In other words, the place doesn't matter. Anyone, Jew or Samaritan, may worship God anywhere. What matters is the spirit in which one worships.

Somehow the conversation turned to the coming of the Messiah.

"I know He is coming," she said, "and when He comes He will tell us all things."

148

SUDDEN HARVEST

She was close to the kingdom now. So very close! And Jesus longed to bring her in.

"I that speak unto thee am he," He said quietly.

What she said in reply we do not know, for at that moment the disciples returned with the food they had bought.

They were amazed to find Him talking to a woman—and such a woman! Didn't He know she was a Samaritan? Didn't He know that she was living a very wicked life? But they didn't say what they thought.

"Master, eat," they said, spreading out the supper before Him.

But He couldn't eat. He was thinking about that poor woman and how near she had come to understanding the truth about Himself and His kingdom. He could still see her running back to the city as fast as she could, and He knew what would happen next.

Then He surprised His disciples by saying, "Say not ye, There are yet four months, and then cometh harvest? behold, I say unto you, Lift up your eyes, and look on the fields; for they are white already to harvest."

What could He mean? they wondered. Of course there were four months before the harvest, but what had that to do with their supper? And how could there be a harvest to gather now?

Then they saw it.

Coming out of the city gates was a crowd of excited people—men and women, boys and girls. They were running toward the well. In their midst was the woman who had been with Jesus just a little while before. At the top of her voice she was shouting, "Come, see a man, which told me all things that ever I did: is not this the Christ?"

What a harvest that was! And how quickly the seed had sprouted! Not four months had been needed to bring forth this rich fruitage but a four-minute talk with Jesus.

On and on the people came, eager to meet the Messiah and hear His message for themselves—a harvest of Samaritans for His kingdom of love!

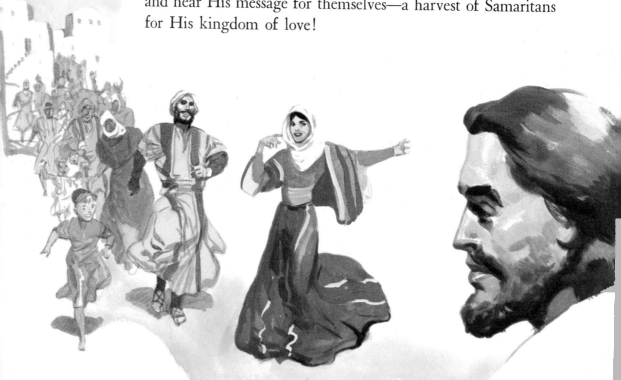

PART IV

Stories of Jesus' Miracles

(MATTHEW 4:23-25; 8:5-34; MARK 1:21-2:12;
4:35-5:20; LUKE 4:14-5:11; 7:1-17; 8:22-40;
JOHN 4:43-54)

STORY 1

Daddy's Prayer Answered

SOON dozens of Samaritans were crowding around Jesus. Boys and girls pressed close to Him, while some struggled for a seat on the wall around the well. Could this stranger really be the Messiah? they wondered.

As Jesus talked about His kingdom of love they listened with growing eagerness. Never had they heard anybody speak like this. This Jesus of Nazareth was so kind, so gentle and, well, so understanding. He seemed to know everything about everybody.

Every boy thought He was talking to *him*. Every girl was sure He was talking to *her*. And the things He said were so simple that even the youngest knew what He was talking about. His words were so beautiful they seemed like living water bubbling up out of Jacob's well.

When at last Jesus said that maybe it was time to go everybody cried, "Oh, no, don't go! Stay and tell us more!"

So Jesus stayed. When darkness fell, the people took

153

← PAINTING BY KREIGH COLLINS   © 1956, BY REVIEW AND HERALD

As Jesus talked about His kingdom of love, the children listened with growing eagerness, for every boy thought He was talking to him, and every girl was sure He was talking to her.

Him back to their village and gave Him the best room they could find.

All next day, and the next, He remained with them. No doubt He went from home to home, comforting the sad and making everybody feel better. We can well believe that before He left there wasn't a single sick person in Sychar.

At last, when Jesus had to leave, tears filled many eyes. Nobody wanted Him to go. The Bible says that "many of the Samaritans believed on him." Turning to the woman who had first told them about Jesus, they said, "Now we believe, not because of thy saying: for we have heard him ourselves, and know that this is indeed the Christ, the Saviour of the world."

Traveling on northward, Jesus came once more to Cana of Galilee where, only a little while before, He had turned water into wine at the marriage feast.

Here He was given a hero's welcome. News of what had happened in Jerusalem had already reached the little city. Everybody was thrilled at the story of how He had overturned the tables of the moneychangers and driven the greedy merchants out of the Temple. It was almost too good to be true that one of themselves, a Galilean, had had the courage to do such a thing!

Then, too, rumors were flying everywhere about the way Jesus had been healing people of all kinds of sicknesses. The Carpenter of Nazareth not only had turned water into wine but had made the blind to see and the deaf to hear! So now the people of Cana crowded around Him, as the villagers of Sychar had done.

154

DADDY'S PRAYER ANSWERED

About one o'clock in the afternoon, as they stood in the market place listening to Jesus, a well-dressed man, evidently in great haste, started to push his way through the crowd. His garments were dusty, for he had just ridden the fourteen miles from Capernaum as fast as he could.

"Excuse me, please," the nobleman was saying, "but I must get through to Him at once. It's very urgent."

The crowd opened to let him through.

"Come and heal my son," he cried to Jesus, "for he is at the point of death."

"Unless you see signs and wonders," said Jesus tenderly, "you will not believe."

"Sir," begged the desperate man, "come down before my child dies!"

How this daddy loved his little boy!

Jesus understood.

"Go," he said to the anxious man, "your son will live."

Maybe it was the way Jesus said it, or perhaps the look in His eyes or the smile on His face; but, whatever it was, the nobleman knew that what He had said was true. He believed the word of Jesus and stopped worrying about his boy, much as he loved him. To prove his faith he stayed in Cana with Jesus the rest of the day, even though his home town was but a three-hour journey away.

Next day this nobleman started out for Capernaum. On the way he met some of his servants coming up the hill. Their happy faces told him that they had good news.

"Your son is well!" they cried eagerly.

"I know," said the nobleman. "But, tell me, when did he begin to get better?"

"At one o'clock yesterday," they said, "the fever left him."

"One o'clock!" murmured the nobleman. "One o'clock!" That was the very moment Jesus had said, "Your son will live." How very, very wonderful! He could hardly wait to get home to see his son and tell him what Jesus had done for him.

The Bible says that not only did he himself believe in Jesus, but "his whole house."

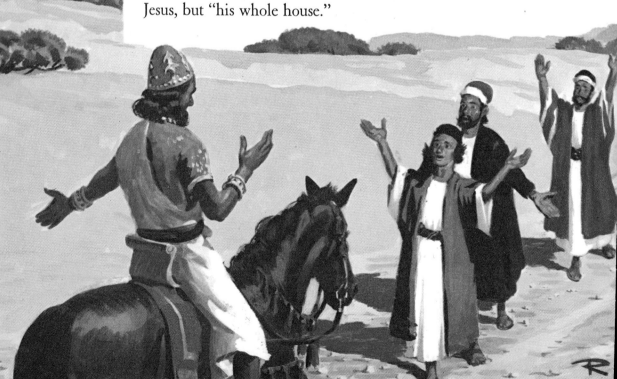

≈≈≈≈≈≈≈≈≈

STORY 2

Madman in Church

≈≈≈≈≈≈≈≈≈≈≈≈≈≈≈≈≈≈

THE synagogue in Capernaum was packed. News had spread that Jesus was going to be there this Sabbath and everybody in town had come to see and hear Him.

Some were there for the usual morning service, but most of those present had come to see the Man who had turned water into wine, healed the sick, and driven the merchants out of the Temple in Jerusalem.

When Jesus began to speak, a hush fell upon the crowd. All eyes were fixed upon this wonderful new Preacher who seemed to have taken the place of John the Baptist, now, alas, in prison.

"The time is fulfilled," said Jesus, breaking the silence, "and the kingdom of God is at hand: repent . . . and believe the gospel."

With the ease and simplicity of a great teacher He showed from the Holy Scriptures that the hour had come for the Messiah to appear; that the time prophecy that Gabriel had re-

157

vealed to Daniel was fulfilled. The Deliverer whom God had promised was among them. The Seed of the woman, promised to Eve in the Garden of Eden, was here to bruise the serpent's head. The Child of destiny, promised by the prophet Isaiah, had been born. He had grown up among them and was now in their midst, ready to do His appointed work.

As Jesus continued to speak, telling how He had come to build a kingdom of goodness, peace, and love—a kingdom to which anybody, anywhere, could belong—the people "were astonished at his doctrine: for he taught them as one that had authority, and not as the scribes."

Suddenly, perhaps as He was saying that anyone who wanted victory over evil could have it for the asking, a terrible shriek rent the air.

All eyes turned to see what was the matter. They saw a madman in the synagogue, his eyes wild, his face twisted in pain. Men tried to lead him out, but he beat them off.

"Let us alone!" he cried to Jesus. "What have you to do with us, Jesus of Nazareth? Have you come to destroy us? I know who you are, the Holy One of God."

Jesus knew that this poor man was possessed by a demon. One of Satan's evil angels was in control of his mind, making him behave like this.

Speaking to the demon, Jesus said, in a voice of command, "Be silent, and come out of him!"

Suddenly the man let out another terrible cry. Then he staggered and fell. But it was the demon's last struggle. In a moment the demon left him.

158

MADMAN IN CHURCH

The madman was now in his right mind. Weakly he looked up into the face of Jesus, pouring out his thanks.

The synagogue service was forgotten. Faced by this new wonder the people could do nothing but talk. With their own eyes they had seen a madman healed! With their own ears they had heard the Carpenter of Nazareth give orders to a demon, and the demon had obeyed Him!

This was the most wonderful thing that had ever happened in Capernaum! The Bible says that "they were all amazed," and said to one another, "What a word is this! for with authority and power he commandeth the unclean spirits, and they come out."

Rushing from the synagogue, they hurried everywhere with the great news. And the fame of Jesus "spread abroad throughout all the region round about Galilee."

STORY 3

Flood Tide of Love

FROM this moment on it seemed as though a flood tide of love was being poured from heaven upon the people of Galilee.

Jesus had come from heaven to earth to let everybody know that God is love, and now He set about it by doing one kindly deed after another. Not only did He talk about God's love, He proved it by healing the people of all their sicknesses, great and small. Often after He had passed through a city or village there wasn't even one sick baby left in any home. For a little while, at least, everyone was well and happy and full of hope.

Boys and girls felt the warmth of His love. Yet He was just as thoughtful of the oldest grandpas and grandmas who came to hear Him.

Opening the floodgates of love kept Him busy every moment. The Bible says that "Jesus went about all Galilee, teaching in their synagogues, and preaching the

160

gospel of the kingdom, and healing all manner of sickness and all manner of disease among the people."

Those who were well "brought unto him all sick people that were taken with divers diseases and torments, and those which were possessed with devils, and those which were lunatick, and those that had the palsy; and he healed them."

In homes all over Palestine, children were talking about Him, saying, "If only we could take Mother to see this wonderful Man, perhaps she would get well again. Perhaps He could do something for her dreadful headaches. And Dad, poor old Dad, with his backache and that sore on his leg, perhaps he could be cured, too. Somehow we must take them both to the Great Healer."

In thousands of homes children and older people were talking like this, wondering how they could find Jesus, then setting out with their sick folks to meet Him.

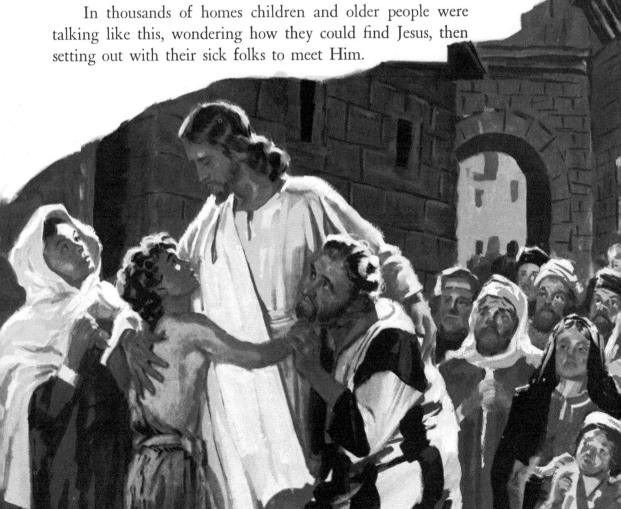

"And there followed him great multitudes of people from Galilee, and from Decapolis, and from Jerusalem, and from Judaea, and from beyond Jordan."

No wonder! Wouldn't you have gone to see Him too if you had lived in those days? Of course you would. And especially if you had toothache, or measles, or polio, or some other disease.

The sick—some hobbling along alone, some riding on donkeys, some being carried by friends—came to Him from all directions and great distances, as if drawn by some powerful magnet. In His presence their groanings ceased; their cries of agony were stilled.

As news about the great Teacher and Healer spread ever farther and farther abroad, more and more thousands came to Him. In His wonderful love "He healed them all." He didn't stop to ask to what race or nation they belonged, or how much money they had, or how great sinners they were. If they needed help and believed that He could give it to them, their wish was granted. He held nothing back from anybody.

"Come unto me, *all* ye that labour and are heavy laden," He said, "and I will give you rest. Take my yoke upon you, and learn of me; for I am meek and lowly in heart: and ye shall find rest unto your souls. For my yoke is easy, and my burden is light."

Rest! That is what they all wanted. Rest from pain, rest from sorrow, rest from worry.

"Come!" He pleaded, "all of you, come!"

162

FLOOD TIDE OF LOVE

They came; and even as they listened to Him their poor, sad hearts were comforted.

One day word reached Jesus that Peter's mother-in-law was ill. Busy as He was, He went straight to her house. The poor woman was very sick, having "a great fever." Jesus took one look at her, then tenderly touched her hand. Immediately "the fever left her," and her strength returned. A moment later she was up and about, waiting on her visitors.

That same evening, "when the sun was setting, all they that had any sick with divers diseases brought them unto him; and he laid his hands on every one of them, and healed them."

"Devils also came out of many, crying out, and saying, Thou art Christ the Son of God."

What a time was that! Earth had never seen the like. The God of love was making Himself known, letting everybody see how kind, and good, and tenderhearted, and forgiving He really was.

He had told Moses long before that "the Lord, the Lord God" is "merciful and gracious, longsuffering, and abundant in goodness and truth, keeping mercy for thousands, forgiving iniquity and transgression and sin." Now everybody could see it with their own eyes. From now on there could be no doubt. God in Christ was all that love could be.

≈≈≈≈≈

STORY 4

Home-Town Boy Returns

≈≈≈≈≈≈≈≈≈≈

B Y AND BY Jesus came to Nazareth again. How glad
He must have been to see His old home town once
more! No doubt He looked in the carpenter's shop
where He had spent so many busy, happy years. Perhaps He
thought it would be nice to open His toolbox and start making
something again. But there was no time for that now.

Hardly had He arrived in town when people began to
crowd around Him. They wanted to see how He had changed
since He had left home. Because He had grown up among
them they found it hard to believe the stories they had heard
about His preaching and healing. Others might think He was
the Son of God, but here He was just the son of Joseph.

When it was rumored that Jesus might speak in the
synagogue on Sabbath, everybody flocked to hear Him. As
He rose to read from the Holy Scriptures He looked upon the
largest congregation that had ever packed the place. Most of
the faces were familiar to Him. He had known these people

165

When Jesus returned to His home town of
Nazareth, the fame of His teaching and healing had gone before Him, and now everyone
flocked to the synagogue to hear Him speak.

all His life. Some were friendly, others critical, but all were curious to hear what the "home-town boy" would say.

Jesus had worshiped in this synagogue all His early life. More than a thousand times He must have walked here from His home on the Sabbath day, first with Joseph and Mary, then with Mary alone, and sometimes by Himself. That is why the Bible says that when He came to Nazareth now He went into the synagogue on the Sabbath day "as His custom was." It had been His custom for a long, long time and this day He gladly followed it again.

Opening the Scriptures to the book of Isaiah, Jesus began to read from the sixty-first chapter, where, according to Luke 4:18, 19, it says: "The Spirit of the Lord is upon me, because he hath anointed me to preach the gospel to the poor; he hath sent me to heal the brokenhearted, to preach deliverance to the captives, and recovering of sight to the blind, to set at liberty them that are bruised, to preach the acceptable year of the Lord."

So tenderly yet forcefully did Jesus read the old, familiar words that everybody was moved by them. So much so that when He closed the book "the eyes of all them that were in the synagogue were fastened upon him."

Then He shocked them with these words: "This day this scripture is fulfilled in your ears."

As the people listened in amazement He applied this famous prophecy to Himself. "I, who have lived among you so long," He said, in effect, "have been anointed by God to do this work and preach this message. Once I mended your furniture; but now I shall mend broken hearts, give sight to the blind, and set the oppressed at liberty."

For a while the beauty of His words and the gentleness of His voice captured the hearts of the people so that they "wondered at the gracious words which proceeded out of his mouth."

Then a change came. Many present hoped He would perform a miracle, as He had in Capernaum and other places. When they heard Him say that God had sent Him to deliver captives and give sight to the blind they felt sure that He would heal somebody then and there. But He didn't.

So they began to find fault. "Is not this Joseph's son?" they whispered. "He's nobody after all! He can't work miracles."

Jesus knew what was going on in their minds and said, in other words, "I know you are saying, Physician, heal yourself; what you did in Capernaum do here also. But no prophet is accepted in his own country."

Then He reminded them that in the days of Elijah it was a widow of *Sidon,* not of Israel, who was fed in the years of famine; and that in the days of Elisha it was Naaman, a *Syrian,* who was healed of leprosy, though there were many lepers in Israel.

What He wanted them to see was that it is not the place where a person lives that matters to God, but the state of his heart. God's miracles are for those of *any* city or *any* nation who believe in Him, and do what He says.

The people got the point at once. It made them angry.

"So He thinks we're not as good as the people of Capernaum!" they whispered. "Well, we'll show Him."

Suddenly the peace and calm of the holy Sabbath was shattered. Men jumped to their feet, shouting at the Preacher. Some left their seats and rushed toward Him. Soon the whole synagogue was in turmoil.

Jesus managed to make His way out in safety, but once on the street He found Himself facing a huge, angry crowd.

"Kill Him!" cried somebody. "Shove Him over the cliff!"

Soon the mob was pushing Jesus to the high ridge near which Nazareth was built.

Things looked bad for a while. It seemed as if Jesus' ministry was going to end almost before it had begun.

But suddenly the crowd halted in confusion. People started shouting at each other, "Where is He? Where's He gone?"

Jesus had disappeared. The Bible says that, "passing through the midst of them," He went His way.

So He left Nazareth. But what a pity that His own city, the place of His childhood and youth, should have treated Him like this! Much as He had wanted to help these people, He couldn't. They wouldn't let Him. A few were blessed by His coming. "He laid his hands upon a few sick folk, and healed them." But He "did not many mighty works there because of their unbelief."

How much they missed by their meanness and folly!

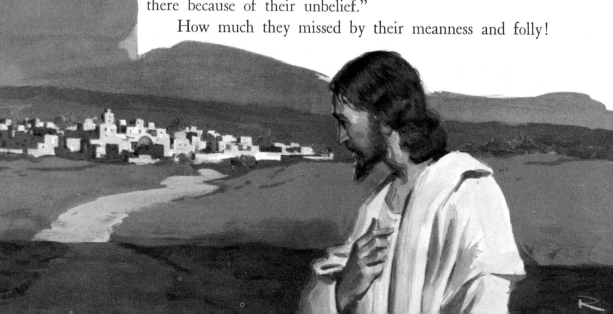

STORY 5

The Master Fisherman

S OME years ago I stood on the shore of Lake Galilee and watched the fishing boats come in. It was early in the morning. The sun was rising over the eastern hills, throwing a golden glow upon the dark, still water.

Then through the mist came the little boats. First one, then another. They were steering for the jetty at Tiberias where at last they all tied up.

I walked on the jetty and looked in the boats. Some had a few fish in them; some had none. The fishermen hadn't had a very successful night, and I couldn't help thinking of that morning in the long ago when Jesus stood on this very spot.

That was when Peter and his friends had also had a bad night's fishing. Not a bite! Not a single fish in their nets!

Coming ashore, they had just begun to wash their nets and get ready for the next night's fishing when they noticed Jesus coming toward them, followed by a crowd of people.

As Jesus stopped near the water's edge the crowd pressed

169

closer and closer until He was in danger of being pushed into the lake. Seeing a boat pulled up on the shore He stepped into it and asked Peter, who was standing nearby, to shove it out a little way.

Peter gladly did so and Jesus "sat down, and taught the people out of the ship."

What a beautiful scene that must have been! The little boats rolling gently to and fro, their sails flapping idly in the breeze. The bright morning sunshine lighting the lovely countryside and mixing a million diamonds in the tiny wavelets that lapped the shore.

On the beach sat scores of men and women, old and young, rich and poor, looking eagerly into the face of Jesus, loving every precious word that fell from His lips.

PAUL REMMEY, ARTIST

In front of them may have been a couple of little girls paddling in the water and a boy trying to float a boat he had cut from a piece of wood. But even they were listening, looking up now and then in the hope that Jesus would smile at them.

How long Jesus spoke we do not know. At last, however, He told the people it was time for them to go. Then, turning to Peter, He said, "Launch out into the deep, and let down your nets for a draught."

Peter looked at Him in surprise. Didn't He know that nobody went fishing in the daytime? Jesus might be a wonderful teacher, but He must surely be a very poor fisherman.

"Master," he said, "we have toiled all the night, and have taken nothing: nevertheless at thy word I will let down the net."

He had no hope of catching any fish at this time of the morning, but he was willing to do anything to please this good, kind Man.

So he and his friends hauled up the anchor and began to row. They didn't go far. It didn't seem worth while. After all, they were only going fishing to humor the Master.

Presently the men stopped rowing and threw the net overboard.

I am sure there must have been a smile on Jesus' face as they did so. He knew what was going to happen. Pretty soon they would find out that He wasn't such a bad fisherman after all.

Meanwhile the men sat around wondering how long they should wait before pulling in the net. They didn't want

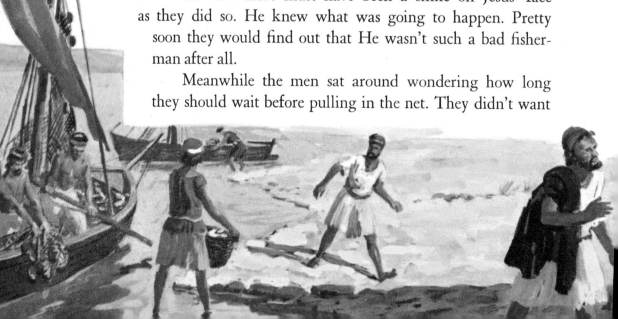

to do it too soon, of course; that wouldn't seem very polite.

How long they left it in the water we do not know. But by and by Peter said, "Better bring it in now," and they all started hauling on the ropes.

Suddenly their eyes opened wide in astonishment. The net was heavy as lead. They had to heave and pull with all their might just to move it a few inches. It was full of fish!

"Look out!" cried Peter. "The net's breaking!"

And so it was. Their strong, well-made net, of which they had been so proud, was splitting right before their eyes.

"Help!" they cried excitedly to the fishermen in the other boat. "Come! Help us get these fish aboard!"

The men in the other boat got out their oars and rowed their hardest toward them. Soon all were wrestling with that bursting net, trying to heave it out of the water. Some of the fish were tipped into one boat, some into the other. This went on until both boats were so full that they began to sink.

With water lapping over the sides of the boats the men rowed for the shore. And when they got there, what do you suppose they did? They forgot all about the fish and the nets and the boats, and fell on their knees before Jesus.

"Depart from me," said Peter, humbly; "for I am a sinful man, O Lord."

"Fear not," Jesus said to him; "from now on you shall catch men."

Their hearts were won. "They forsook all, and followed him."

STORY 6

The Man With Five Friends

ONE day Jesus was invited into a very nice home in Capernaum to meet some famous people. Pharisees and "doctors of the law" had gathered here "out of every town of Galilee, and Judaea and Jerusalem."

These church leaders had heard a great deal about Jesus and they wanted to meet Him. With the whole countryside talking about this new Teacher and Healer they felt that they must find out about Him for themselves.

Most of them no doubt were old men, with long, gray beards. Beside them Jesus, only thirty years of age, must have seemed quite young. Can't you see them peering at Him with keen, critical eyes, wondering how this humble-looking Carpenter of Nazareth could do the things people said He had done?

At last Jesus began to speak, but it was difficult to make Himself heard. There were so many people outside clamoring to get in. It seemed as if the whole town knew He was

174

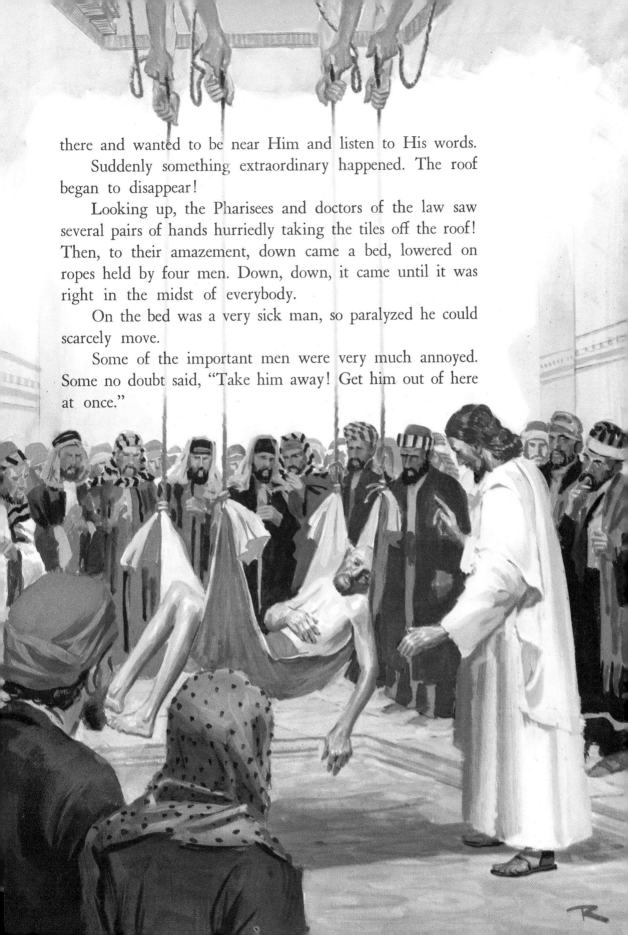

there and wanted to be near Him and listen to His words.

Suddenly something extraordinary happened. The roof began to disappear!

Looking up, the Pharisees and doctors of the law saw several pairs of hands hurriedly taking the tiles off the roof! Then, to their amazement, down came a bed, lowered on ropes held by four men. Down, down, it came until it was right in the midst of everybody.

On the bed was a very sick man, so paralyzed he could scarcely move.

Some of the important men were very much annoyed. Some no doubt said, "Take him away! Get him out of here at once."

But the sick man was lying helpless on his bed, and Jesus' tender heart was full of pity for him.

Knowing the true cause of the poor man's sickness, Jesus said to him, "Man, thy sins are forgiven thee."

"Blasphemy!" whispered one of the old men. "Who can forgive sins, but God alone?"

Jesus knew what they were all thinking and asked them, "Which is easier, to say, Thy sins be forgiven thee; or to say, Rise up and walk?"

None of them could answer Him. So Jesus told them He would let them see that the Son of man had power on earth to forgive sins. Turning to the sick man, He told him to get up, take up his bed, and go home.

Instantly the man leaped to his feet, perfectly well, and ran away "glorifying God."

I hope he stopped long enough to thank his friends. For he had five of them. The four who had let him down through the roof and Jesus who had restored him to health and strength.

As for the old men "they were all amazed, and they glorified God, and were filled with fear, saying, We have seen strange things to day."

STORY 7

The Centurion's Servant

ONE day while Jesus was in Capernaum an officer in the Roman Army asked for His help. He was a centurion, which means that he was captain of a company of one hundred soldiers. Most likely he was the most important Roman officer in the city.

As an officer, it was his duty to keep the peace. He had been watching Jesus ever since He first came to Capernaum and began His work. No doubt he had stood in the crowd and listened as Jesus taught the people. He had had to make sure that this Galilean wasn't saying anything that might lead the people to rebel against Rome.

As he had listened he had come to respect Jesus very highly. Here, he was sure, was a very good Man, and a very great Man. The kingdom of love He talked about was no threat to Rome. Rome could do with some of this love.

When his servant became ill, and the doctors could do nothing more for him, the centurion thought of Jesus and remembered the stories of His power to heal the sick.

But, he wondered, would Jesus be willing to help an officer in the hated Roman army? Did His love reach beyond the Jews? Well, it was worth trying.

First, he sent to the Jewish leaders and asked them to speak to Jesus for him. They did so, adding that this man was worthy of help because "He loves our nation and has built us a synagogue."

But the centurion didn't think he was worthy. When Jesus drew near his house he sent another messenger to say, very humbly, "Lord, do not trouble yourself, for I am not worthy to have you come under my roof. Just say the word and my servant will be healed. For I am a man under authority, with soldiers under me; and I say to one, 'Go,' and he goes, and to another, 'Come,' and he comes, and to my servant, 'Do this,' and he does it."

At this Jesus marveled, and turning to those about Him said, "I have not found so great faith, no, not in Israel."

This centurion, a Roman soldier, was the first to see that Jesus was not only a Healer and a Teacher but a Ruler and a King. He had seen more in Jesus than the Jews, whose Messiah He was. That is why Jesus went on to say, "Many shall come from the east and west, and shall sit down with Abraham, and Isaac, and Jacob, in the kingdom of heaven. But the children of the kingdom shall be cast out."

By this He meant that people of many nations and countries will accept Him as their Lord while others close at hand, who should know better, will reject Him.

178

THE CENTURION'S SERVANT

Pleased by the centurion's amazing faith, and wishing to teach His hearers a lesson, Jesus turned to him and said, "Go; be it done for you as you have believed."

The centurion had said that he believed Jesus could heal his servant at a distance, without even coming to the house. He was sure Jesus had but to say the word and the sick man would be healed. And so it happened. As soon as Jesus commended the centurion for his faith, at that very moment his servant was healed.

I can imagine the servant jumping out of his bed, his pain all gone, his face wreathed in smiles.

"Thank you, thank you!" I can hear him saying to his master.

"Don't thank me," I am sure the noble centurion replied; "thank the wonderful Carpenter of Nazareth."

STORY 8

The Interrupted Funeral

NEXT day, to the surprise of His friends, Jesus left Capernaum for the little city of Nain, some twenty miles away. This meant a long uphill climb, and no doubt His disciples, who walked beside and behind Him, wondered why He had suddenly decided to go on this tiresome trip.

They did not know that a widow's son had just died there, but Jesus did.

As they trudged along the rugged mountain trail the group of followers grew larger and larger until, as the Bible says, "A great crowd went with him."

There was magic in the name of Jesus. Workers in the fields dropped their tools and hurried to join the passing procession. Women ran out of their houses at the sound of His voice. The sick followed too, leaning on friends, hoping to be healed. Boys and girls came in droves to see what was going on. It was a great day for everybody.

180

THE INTERRUPTED FUNERAL

As the vast company drew near to Nain another procession was seen coming out of the city gate. It was a funeral.

One group was following the Prince of life; the other a dead body on its way to the cemetery. One was made up of happy, expectant people; the other of weeping, despairing ones. It was like a river of life flowing into a river of death. Something was bound to happen.

From the size of the funeral procession it seemed as though almost everybody in the city must have decided to show their respect for the dead youth and their sympathy for his mother, who was a widow. All were sad that she had lost her only son.

Could it be that Jesus was acquainted with this poor woman and her son? Why not? And might He not have timed His arrival at Nain to bring her help just when hope seemed gone? So much does He know about us all, so greatly does He love and care!

As the two processions met, Jesus came face to face with the poor widow. She was walking close behind the bier, or litter, on which her dead boy lay; and she was weeping bitterly.

As Jesus stopped to speak to her the crowd behind Him surged forward. A moment later He, the woman, and the dead boy, were in the center of a seething multitude, all trying to see what was going on.

"Do not cry," Jesus said to the widow, in deep compassion. And there was something in His voice that seemed to say, "You don't need to cry any more; I have a surprise for you."

Then He touched the bier and spoke to the corpse upon it. Now His voice rang like a command. "Young man, I say to you, Arise!"

Suddenly the dead youth moved. His eyes opened. Then he sat up and began to talk. Terrified, the bearers dropped the bier and fled into the crowd. The next moment mother and son were in each other's arms, weeping tears of joy at this wonderful event.

Those who saw the astounding miracle were struck with awe. The look of amazement on their faces must have been something to see. For a while everybody, men and women, boys and girls, were speechless. Then the silence was broken by a murmur that grew louder and louder as one person passed the news to another, clear to the back of the crowd.

"He raised the dead!" people whispered. "He even raised the dead!"

"He told the boy to come to life, and he did!"

"He gave the widow back her son! How kind of Him!"

"He stopped a funeral! Who ever heard of such a thing!"

"Surely a great prophet has arisen among us! God has visited His people!"

Meanwhile the widow and her son were struggling to make their way back to the city through the crowds of people who were trying to catch a glimpse of them.

How happy they were! Jesus had turned their night into day, their sorrow into joy.

STORY 9

Lord of the Winds and Waves

ONE evening, after a busy day of teaching and healing, Jesus said to His disciples, "Let's get in a boat
and go to the other side of the lake." He was weary,
and longed to get away to some quiet spot where He could
rest awhile.

But it was hard to persuade the people to go home. They
just stayed and stayed and stayed, enjoying every minute in
His presence. Like children at bedtime they kept on asking
for more and more stories. At last, however, the disciples made
them understand that Jesus simply couldn't talk to them any
more that day. He just had to have a rest.

As the crowds began to drift away, the disciples helped
Jesus "even as he was" into one of the boats and pushed off
from the land. Other little boats set off at the same time, no
doubt filled with people who had made up their minds to
follow Him wherever He might go.

Tired out, Jesus went to the back of the boat and lay down

184

on a pillow. A moment later He was fast asleep.

It was a beautiful evening. The sun went down behind the western hills in a blaze of glory. Darkness fell, and the stars came out. A gentle breeze filled the sails, carrying all the boats toward the land of Gadara.

Then, suddenly, the weather changed, as it does on Galilee even today. In less time than it takes to tell, a storm swept down the mountains, turning the peaceful lake into a wild and dangerous sea. Dark clouds rushed across the sky, blotting out the stars. Thunder roared. Lightning flashed. The breeze became a hurricane, whipping up great waves that swept over the boats, filling them with water.

So bad was the storm that even Peter, James, John, and the other disciples, who had grown up on the lake, were frightened. It was

the worst night they had ever known. Despair seized them. They felt sure this was the end.

Then they remembered Jesus.

Oddly enough He was still asleep. Even the loudest thunderclaps had not awakened Him. Nor had the fearful rolling and tossing disturbed Him.

As the water rose higher and higher in the boat, despite their best efforts to bail it out, the disciples felt they could stand it no longer. Jesus must be aroused.

Shouting above the noise of the gale one of them cried, "Master, don't you care that we perish?"

Jesus stood up, His feet in the water that was sloshing from side to side of the boat.

"Lord, save us, we perish!" cried the disciples—a cry Jesus never fails to answer.

Looking around at the dark, angry sky and the fearful white-capped waves, He said, in a voice of command, "Peace, be still!"

Suddenly, as quickly as it had come up, the storm died away "and there was a great calm."

In words of gentle rebuke Jesus said to His disciples, "Why are you afraid? Have you no faith?"

There was nothing they could say to this. They just went on baling out the water, whispering in awe one to another, "Who then is this, that even the wind and the sea obey Him!"

No wonder! Never had they heard anyone order the elements about like this. Never indeed had it been done since creation, when God said, "Let there be light," "Let there be

187

← PAINTING BY WILLIAM HUTCHINSON © 1956, BY REVIEW AND HERALD

As the great storm swept over the Sea of Galilee, and threatened to capsize the boat, the disciples cried out in fear. Then Jesus calmed the tempest with the words, "Peace, be still."

a firmament," "Let the waters bring forth abundantly," "Let the earth bring forth the living creature after his kind." Now the Creator had spoken again, and creation had recognized His voice.

What happened to all the people in the other little boats? The Bible does not say. But they must have had a very bad time. If Peter was afraid, I am sure they were too. No doubt they also cried for help. Certainly when the great calm came they were greatly comforted. Perhaps Jesus was thinking of them too when He told the wind and waves to be still. I believe He was. For He never forgets the people in the other little boats.

In all the storms of life Jesus is never far away. The little prayer, "Lord, save me!" will bring Him swiftly to our rescue.

STORY 10

Lunatics Made Sane

AS MORNING dawned, calm and beautiful, the boat in which Jesus and His disciples had crossed the lake glided into a sheltered cove on the eastern shore.

Everything seemed so peaceful after the wild and terrible night that all on board looked forward to a quiet and restful day. But it was not to be.

Hardly had they started up the trail into the foothills when two lunatics rushed at them out of a cemetery, where they had been hiding among the tombs.

They were a fearful sight. Madness was in their eyes and voices. Blood flowed over their naked bodies where they had cut themselves with stones. Broken chains, fettered around their wrists and ankles, clanked as they ran.

Most people would have fled in terror from such hideous, dangerous men. But not Jesus. He was not afraid of anybody or anything. He could sleep through a storm at sea or stand calmly while a couple of lunatics ran toward Him.

These poor men were actually possessed by devils, who recognized Jesus at once. "What do you want of us, O Son of God?" they cried as they drew near Him. "Have you come to torment us before the time?"

They knew that Christ was their master and that they were powerless in His presence. They knew, too, that He would cast them out of the men whose minds they now controlled. So they asked if they might be allowed to enter a herd of swine that was feeding nearby.

Jesus gave permission, and suddenly the herd of swine became as mad as the two men had been. Charging crazily hither and yon, they plunged at last down a steep place into the lake and were drowned.

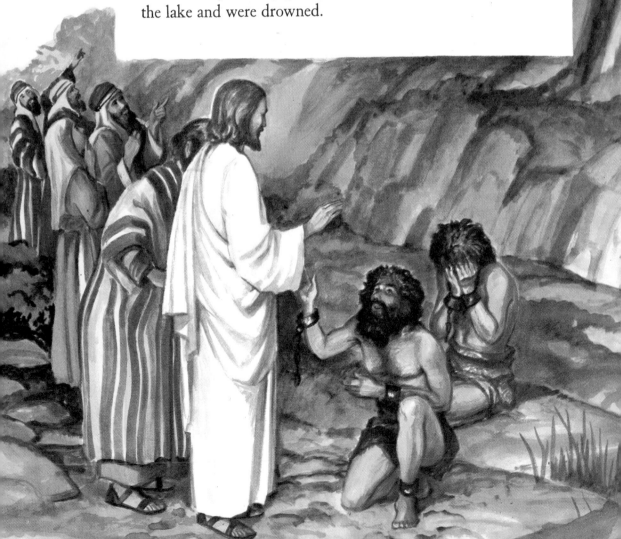

News of this miracle was carried to the nearest town by the swineherds, who feared they would be blamed for the loss of the animals.

Very excited, the people came running to find out what had happened. They saw an amazing sight. Their pigs had disappeared, but the two lunatics, who for years had been the terror of the neighborhood, were sitting at the feet of Jesus, clothed and in their right minds.

No doubt the disciples had shared their own clothes with them and helped them clean up in the waters of the lake. In any case, here they were, perfectly sane and normal.

The city people were filled with fear, and begged Jesus to go away. They were afraid they might lose more of their pigs if He stayed around much longer. It did not occur to them—at least, not then—that if He were to stay among them, He might bring help to other poor souls in need.

So much fuss did they make that Jesus agreed to leave at once.

As He made His way down to the boat the two men whom He had healed begged to be allowed to go along with Him.

But Jesus would not let them. "No," He said, "but go back to your homes and tell all your friends and loved ones what God has done for you."

So they stood on the shore and waved good-by as the boat sailed away. Then they did as Jesus had told them. They went back home and told everybody "how great things the Lord had done" for them.

They were the first missionaries Jesus ever sent out, and certainly among the best. So well did they tell their story that soon everybody for miles around was talking about Jesus and longing to see Him. Those who had asked Him to go away were ashamed of what they had done. And when some time later Jesus returned to Gadara "they were all waiting for Him" and everybody "received Him gladly."

It just shows how much two people can do when they start talking about the great things Jesus has done for them.

These two men who had once been lunatics made all the people of Gadara long to meet Jesus.

Has Jesus done something great for you? Has He shown His love for you in one way or another? Has He given you a "right mind" when you were being angry or foolish? Has He helped you to get rid of some bad habit? Then why not tell everybody about it? Who knows what the result may be? Your brave witness may lead thousands to Him.

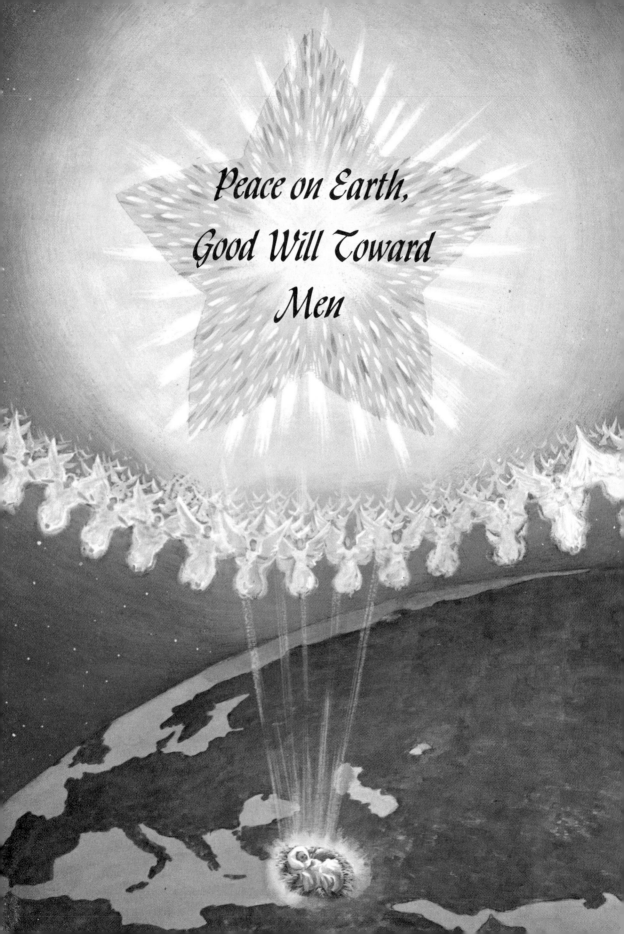